Workbook
Progress in Mathematics

Catherine D. LeTourneau

with

Elinor R. Ford

Sadlier-Oxford
A Division of William H. Sadlier, Inc.
www.sadlier-oxford.com

Contents

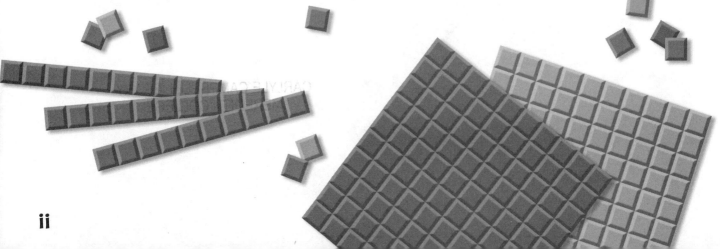

CHAPTER 5 Division Concepts and Facts

CHAPTER 6 More Multiplication and Division Facts

CHAPTER 7 Statistics and Probability

CHAPTER 8 Measurement and Time

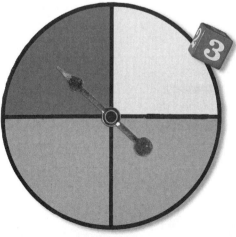

$\frac{1}{10}$ $\frac{1}{8}$ $\frac{1}{4}$

Hundreds

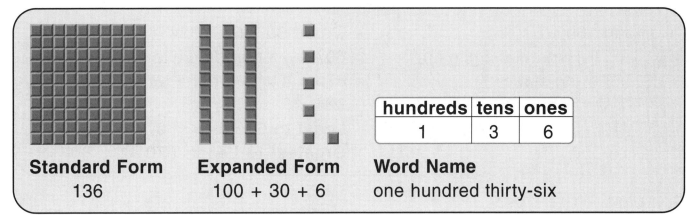

Standard Form
136

Expanded Form
100 + 30 + 6

Word Name
one hundred thirty-six

hundreds	tens	ones
1	3	6

Write the number in standard form.

1. two hundred thirty-nine __239__

2. six hundred forty __640__

3. four hundred sixty-one __461__

4. nine hundred five __905__

5. seven hundred __700__

6. one hundred seven __107__

7. 400 + 4 __404__

8. 900 + 20 + 3 __923__

9. 800 + 80 + 1 __881__

10. 500 + 80 __580__

11. 100 + 90 + 9 __199__

12. 600 + 50 + 2 __652__

Complete. Write each in expanded form.

13. 701 = __7__ hundreds __0__ tens __1__ one = __700__ + __0__ + __1__

14. 383 = __3__ hundreds __8__ tens __3__ ones = __300__ + __80__ + __3__

15. 490 = __4__ hundreds __9__ tens __0__ ones = __400__ + __90__ + __0__

Write the place and the value of the underlined digit.

16. 365 __ones; 5__

17. 753 __hundreds; 700__

18. 502 __tens; 0__

19. 498 __tens; 90__

20. 631 __hundreds; 600__

21. 840 __ones; 0__

 1

Compare Numbers;
Order Numbers

Compare: 607, 670	Order: 607, 670, 624
	607 Hundreds digits are the same.

Compare: 607, 670

h	t	o
6	0	7
6	7	0

Hundreds digits are the same.
Compare the tens: 0 < 7
So 607 < 670.

Order: 607, 670, 624
607 Hundreds digits are the same.
670 Compare the tens: 0 < 2 < 7
624
Least to Greatest: 607, 624, 670
Greatest to Least: 670, 624, 607

Compare. Write < or >.

1. 16 ___<___ 19
2. 25 ___>___ 20
3. 190 ___>___ 160

4. 25 ___<___ 32
5. 10 ___<___ 28
6. 84 ___>___ 48

7. 18 ___<___ 81
8. 17 ___>___ 13
9. 705 ___<___ 806

10. 561 ___<___ 565
11. 876 ___>___ 678
12. 908 ___<___ 980

Write in order from least to greatest.

13. 20, 80, 40   ___20___ ___40___ ___80___

14. 92, 76, 79   ___76___ ___79___ ___92___

15. 327, 486, 418   ___327___ ___418___ ___486___

16. 563, 569, 560   ___560___ ___563___ ___569___

Write in order from greatest to least.

17. 30, 90, 20   ___90___ ___30___ ___20___

18. 66, 18, 68   ___68___ ___66___ ___18___

19. 295, 614, 641   ___641___ ___614___ ___295___

20. 821, 824, 800   ___824___ ___821___ ___800___

Problem Solving

21. Pamela has 525 stickers. Pierre has 550.
Who has more?   ___525 < 550; Pierre___

---

2   **Use with Lessons 1-2 and 1-3, text pages 32–35.**

Counting Patterns

Count by 2s.

1 2️⃣ 3 4️⃣ 5 6️⃣ 7 8️⃣ 9 🔟 11 12️⃣ 13 14️⃣ 15

Count by 3s.

1 2 3️⃣ 4 5 6️⃣ 7 8 9️⃣ 10 11 12️⃣ 13 14 15️⃣

Count by 3s. Write the numbers.

1. Start at 39. End at 54. _39, 42, 45, 48, 51, 54_

2. Start at 60. End at 45. _60, 57, 54, 51, 48, 45_

Count by 4s. Write the numbers.

3. Start at 40. End at 60. _40, 44, 48, 52, 56, 60_

4. Start at 96. End at 76. _96, 92, 88, 84, 80, 76_

Write the missing numbers.

5. 24, 26, _28_, 30, 32, _34_   **6.** 9, 11, 13, _15_, _17_, _19_

7. 95, 90, 85, _80_, _75_, _70_   **8.** 35, 45, 55, _65_, _75_, _85_

9. 13, 16, 19, _22_, 25, _28_, _31_   **10.** 10, 15, _20_, 25, _30_

Problem Solving

11. I am an odd number between 22 and 29.
You say me when you count by 3s.
What number am I? _____27_____

12. I am an even number between 66 and 69.
You say me when you count by 4s.
What number am I? _____68_____

 3

Thousands

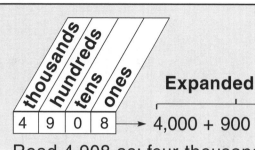

Expanded Form   Standard Form

4 | 9 | 0 | 8 → 4,000 + 900 + 0 + 8 = 4,908

Read 4,908 as: four thousand, nine hundred eight.

Write the number in standard form.

1. 6 thousands 1 hundred 4 tens 6 ones   6,146

2. 9 thousands 0 hundreds 2 tens 0 ones   9,020

3. one thousand, four hundred fifty-eight   1,458

4. eight thousand, thirty   8,030   **5.** six thousand, five   6,005

6. 1,000 + 900 + 30 + 1   1,931   **7.** 7,000 + 0 + 20 + 3   7,023

8. 3,000 + 0 + 0 + 3   3,003   **9.** 9,000 + 500 + 80 + 7   9,587

Write the number in both standard and expanded forms.

10. three thousand, seven hundred thirty-four   3,734; 3,000 + 700 + 30 + 4

11. six thousand, one hundred ninety-eight   6,198; 6,000 + 100 + 90 + 8

12. five thousand, five hundred five   5,505; 5,000 + 500 + 0 + 5

Write the place and the value of the underlined digit.

13. 9,025   thousands; 9,000   **14.** 3,641   hundreds; 600

15. 6,511   tens; 10   **16.** 7,064   thousands; 7,000

17. 8,059   hundreds; 0   **18.** 5,918   ones; 8

19. 1,704   tens; 0   **20.** 2,546   thousands; 2,000

4   **Use with Lesson 1-6, text pages 40–41.**

Ten Thousands and Hundred Thousands

Name _____

Date _____

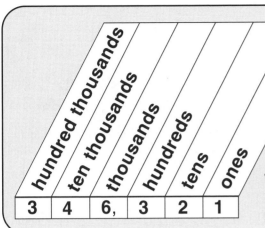

3	4	6,	3	2	1

Expanded Form: 300,000 + 40,000 + 6,000 + 300 + 20 + 1

Standard Form: 346,321

Word Name: three hundred forty-six thousand, three hundred twenty-one

Write how many thousands.

1. 80,000 = ____80____ thousands

2. 95,000 = ____95____ thousands

3. 10,000 = ____10____ thousands

4. 73,000 = ____73____ thousands

5. 655,000 = ____655____ thousands

6. 838,000 = ____838____ thousands

7. 331,000 = ____331____ thousands

8. 444,000 = ____444____ thousands

Write each number in expanded form.

9. 79,462 __7__ ten thousands __9__ thousands __4__ hundreds __6__ tens __2__ ones

10. 193,182 __1__ hundred thousands __9__ ten thousands __3__ thousands __1__ hundreds __8__ tens __2__ ones

Write the number in standard form.

11. 3 ten thousands ____30,000____

12. 9 hundred thousands ____900,000____

13. 20,000 + 4000 + 700 + 10 + 6 ____24,716____

14. 400,000 + 30,000 + 3000 + 200 + 0 + 4 ____433,204____

15. seventy-one thousand, four hundred fifty-six ____71,456____

Write the place and the value of the underlined digit.

16. 945,3̲04 ____hundreds; 300____

17. 3̲86,297 ____hundred thousands; 300,000____

18. 856,73̲1 ____tens; 30____

19. 7̲3̲6,088 ____ten thousands; 30,000____

Compare and Order Larger Numbers

Name _____

Date _____

> Compare: 23,517 _?_ 22,137
>
> Compare ten thousands: 20,000 = 20,000
> Compare thousands: 3000 > 2000
>
> So 23,517 > 22,137.

> Order from least to greatest:
> 6378, 6972, 3001
>
> 3000 < 6000 —→ 3001 is least.
> 6972 > 6378 —→ 6972 is greatest.
> From least to greatest: 3001, 6378, 6972

Compare. Write < or >.

1. 6321 __>__ 2814

2. 4228 __>__ 2488

3. 8330 __<__ 8333

4. 5432 __>__ 5342

5. 6123 __>__ 4151

6. 7251 __=__ 7251

7. 28,115 __<__ 38,110

8. 92,420 __<__ 93,417

9. 62,014 __>__ 57,755

10. 942,963 __>__ 942,657

11. 307,521 __>__ 307,261

12. 163,184 __<__ 163,791

Write in order from to least to greatest.

13. 6661, 2228, 7777   2228   6661   7777

14. 8000, 5000, 9000   5000   8000   9000

15. 38,024, 35,601, 49,237   35,601   38,024   49,237

16. 24,681, 24,087, 24,586   24,087   24,586   24,681

17. 180,149, 180,361, 180,000   180,000   180,149   180,361

Write in order from greatest to least.

18. 8325, 9325, 8625   9325   8625   8325

19. 4996, 4986, 4998   4998   4996   4986

20. 50,008, 50,010, 50,900   50,900   50,010   50,008

21. 264,134, 269,143, 259,431   269,143   264,134   259,431

Round Numbers

Name _____

Date _____

Round to the nearest thousand.

7300

| 3 < 5 |
| Round **down** to 7000. |

1500

| 5 = 5 |
| Round **up** to 2000. |

4800

| 8 > 5 |
| Round **up** to 5000. |

Round to the nearest ten.

1. 43 _____ 40
2. 75 _____ 80
3. 97 _____ 100

4. 31 _____ 30
5. 66 _____ 70
6. 372 _____ 370

7. 506 _____ 510
8. 868 _____ 870
9. 455 _____ 460

10. 638 _____ 640
11. 493 _____ 490
12. 114 _____ 110

Round to the nearest hundred.

13. 452 _____ 500
14. 824 _____ 800
15. 119 _____ 100

16. 798 _____ 800
17. 555 _____ 600
18. 673 _____ 700

19. 274 _____ 300
20. 321 _____ 300
21. 418 _____ 400

22. 638 _____ 600
23. 497 _____ 500
24. 853 _____ 900

Round to the nearest thousand.

25. 4521 _____ 5000
26. 9267 _____ 9000
27. 1865 _____ 2000

28. 8650 _____ 9000
29. 3264 _____ 3000
30. 7202 _____ 7000

31. 2580 _____ 3000
32. 5999 _____ 6000
33. 6435 _____ 6000

34. 1662 _____ 2000
35. 2314 _____ 2000
36. 3537 _____ 4000

Use with Lesson 1-9, text pages 46–47. 7

Coins and Bills

Name _____

Date _____

Find the total amount.

Count on: $5.00 ⟶ $6.00 ⟶ $6.25 ⟶ $6.35 ⟶ $6.40 ⟶ $6.45
The total amount is $6.45.

Write the amount. Use the dollar sign ($) and decimal point (.).

1.

$2.47

2.

$5.60

3.

$10.50

4.

$10.29

5. 3 one-dollar bills, 4 dimes, 3 nickels — $3.55

6. 1 five-dollar bill, 1 quarter, 3 dimes — $5.55

7. 1 ten-dollar bill, 5 dimes, 5 nickels — $10.75

8. 4 ten-dollar bills, 1 half-dollar, 9 pennies — $40.59

9. 2 five-dollar bills, 2 quarters — $10.50

Problem Solving

10. Lin wants to buy a book that costs $5.75. She has 1 five-dollar bill and 4 quarters. How much money does she have?

$5.00 ⟶ $5.25 ⟶ 5.50 ⟶
$5.75 ⟶ $6.00;
$6.00

Make and Count Change

Name _____

Date _____

Dana buys crayons for $3.65. She gives the cashier $5.00.
What is her change? How much is her change?

$3.65 $3.75 $4.00 $5.00

└── +10¢ ──┘ └── +25¢ ──┘ └── +$1.00 ──┘

Arrange the money in order.
Count the change.
Her change is $1.35.

Choose the correct change.

1. Trena rode the Ferris wheel for 35¢. She gave the ticket collector $1.00.

a.

b.

2. Fred spent $1.40 at the food booth. He gave the man 1 dollar, 2 quarters.

a.

b.

Problem Solving **Write the change each receives. Use the menu to solve.**

Answers may vary.

3. Jill gave the clerk $5.00 for a salad and a yogurt. What change does she receive?

  a. Use no quarters.
    $1.76; 1 dollar, 7 dimes, 6 pennies

  b. Use no dimes. $1.76;
    6 pennies, 4 nickels, 2 quarters, 1 dollar

4. Whitney buys an apple. She gives the cashier 2 quarters. ___1 penny, 2 dimes___

5. James buys yogurt. He gives the clerk $1.00. ___1 quarter___

6. Courtney buys a salad. She gives the cashier $3.00. ___1 penny, 2 quarters___

7. Paul buys a carton of milk. He gives the clerk 3 quarters. ___2 dimes___

Cafeteria Menu

Sandwich $2.25

Salad $2.49

Yogurt 75¢

Apple 29¢

Milk 55¢

Compare and Round Money

Name _____

Date _____

Compare: $1.43 _?_ $1.49

Compare dollars: $1.00 = $1.00
Compare dimes: $.40 = $.40
Compare pennies: $.03 < $.09

So $1.43 < $1.49.

Round to the nearest dollar.

$7.23 $34.68
2 < 5   6 > 5
round *down*   round *up*
$7.00 $35.00

Compare. Write < or > .

1. $6.56 __<__ $8.10   **2.** $3.98 __>__ $2.98   **3.** $5.47 __<__ $7.45

4. $4.77 __>__ $4.67   **5.** $9.25 __>__ $9.16   **6.** $1.35 __>__ $1.25

7. $8.33 __<__ $8.37   **8.** $6.74 __>__ $6.54   **9.** $4.58 __>__ $4.52

10. $3.77 __<__ $3.79   **11.** $5.92 __>__ $5.90   **12.** $2.63 __<__ $2.64

13. $8.68 __<__ $8.69   **14.** $7.29 __<__ $7.39   **15.** $1.56 __<__ $6.51

Round to the nearest dollar.

16. $6.51 $7.00   **17.** $1.73 $2.00   **18.** $4.39 $4.00   **19.** $8.25 $8.00

20. $3.34 $3.00   **21.** $7.58 $8.00   **22.** $2.95 $3.00   **23.** $5.08 $5.00

24. $92.16 $92.00   **25.** $67.64 $68.00   **26.** $12.39 $12.00   **27.** $47.52 $48.00

Problem Solving

28. Ramon earned $8.75 raking leaves.
Susie earned $8.35 raking leaves.

a. Who earned more?

$8.75 > $8.35; Ramon

b. Round each amount to the nearest
dollar.

Ramon $9.00; Susie $8.00

Problem-Solving Strategy: Draw A Picture

Name _____

Date _____

Allan is using 22 squares of material to make a small quilt.
Every 4th square is red. How many squares are red?
Draw 22 squares. Mark every 4th square. Count the number of squares you mark.

☐ ☐ ☐ ☒ ☐ ☐ ☐ ☒ ☐ ☐ ☐ ☒ ☐ ☐ ☐ ☒ ☐ ☐ ☐ ☒ ☐ ☐

Five squares are red.

Solve. Do your work on a separate sheet of paper. Check students' drawings.

1. Isabel's father gave her 5 dimes, 1 nickel, and 5 pennies. How much money did he give her?

   60¢ or $.60

2. Carmen had 24 flowers. She put 3 flowers in each vase. How many vases did she use?

   8 vases

3. Don is planning a party for 6 friends. He will serve each friend 2 tuna sandwiches. How many sandwiches does he need to make for his friends?

   12 sandwiches

4. Jenny is making a bracelet with 20 beads. Every 5th bead is purple. How many purple beads will she need?

   4 purple beads

5. Isaiah is making a pattern with the same number of red, white, blue, and green triangles. He uses 32 triangles. How many does he use of each color?

   8 triangles

6. Yushiro made a tower with 25 red and black blocks. He started with a red block. Every other block was red. How many red blocks did he use?

   13 red blocks

7. Ben saved $2.41. Then he found 3 nickels and 9 pennies under his bed. How much money does he have now?

   $2.65

8. Jasmine helped her mother put 2 sheets of paper in each of 8 envelopes. How many sheets of paper did she use?

   16 sheets

Problem-Solving
Applications: Mixed Review

Name _____

Date _____

Solve each problem and explain the method you used. If needed, do all your work on a separate sheet of paper.

Read Plan Solve Check

Strategy File

Use These Strategies
Find a Pattern
Draw a Picture
Make a Table
Use More Than One Step

1. Brian's truck weighs 5394 pounds. Michelle's limousine weighs 5933 pounds. Which vehicle is heavier?

   5394 < 5933; Michelle's limousine

2. A ticket to ride the Ferris Wheel costs $2.50. Jose has a 1 one-dollar bill, 2 half dollars, and 6 dimes. Does Jose have enough money for a ride?

   $1.00 → $1.50 → $2.00 → $2.60
   $2.60 > $2.50; yes

3. The flight from Boston to San Francisco is three thousand, one hundred forty-seven miles. Write this as a standard numeral.

   3,147

4. Andre is reading a book that has 445 pages. Philip's book has four hundred fifty pages. Which book is longer?

   445 < 450; Philip's book

5. Every fourth vehicle in the library parking lot is a minivan. There are 28 cars parked in the lot. How many of the vehicles are minivans?

   7 minivans

6. Barney and Sue spent $27.62 to set up a carwash. At the end of the day they had 1 ten-dollar bill, 3 five-dollar bills, 1 half dollar, 6 quarters, and 20 nickels. Did they make a profit?

   $10.00 → $15.00 → $20.00 →
   $25.00 → $25.50 → $27.00 →
   $28.00 $28.00 > $27.62; yes

7. Margie is cooking microwave popcorn. 35 kernels pop during the first minute of cooking, 70 during the second, and 105 during the third. If the popcorn continues to pop at this rate, how many kernels will pop in the fifth minute?

   175 kernels

8. Ohio State University's football stadium has 101,568 seats. The University of Michigan's football stadium has 107,501 seats. Which stadium has more seats?

   101,568 < 107,501;
   Michigan's

9. A roll of nickels from a bank is worth 2 dollars. A roll of dimes is worth 5 dollars. How many more coins are in a roll of dimes than a roll of nickels?

   40 nickels = $2.00; 50 dimes =
   $5.00; 50 − 40 = 10 more

More Than Two Addends; Missing Addends

Name _____

Date _____

6 + 4 + 5 + 1 = _?_ **Add down.** 6 4 6 + 4 = **10** 5 10 + 5 = **15** +1 15 + 1 = **16** 16	Find the missing addend. 7 + _?_ = 13 Think: 13 − 7 = ? 13 − 7 = 6 7 + 6 = 13

Add.

1. 7	**2.** 2	**3.** 6	**4.** 4	**5.** 5	**6.** 1
3	8	1	4	3	9
+5	+7	+9	6	2	5
15	17	16	+3	+5	+3
			17	15	18

7. 6 + 2 + 8 = _16_   **8.** 5 + 7 + 1 = _13_   **9.** 4 + 3 + 9 = _16_

10. 9 + 1 + 4 + 5 = _19_   **11.** 3 + 6 + 1 + 7 = _17_   **12.** 5 + 2 + 3 + 0 = _10_

Find the sum.

13. 6¢	**14.** 7¢	**15.** 9¢	**16.** 5¢	**17.** 8¢	**18.** 4¢
4¢	8¢	4¢	6¢	1¢	0¢
3¢	1¢	1¢	1¢	4¢	7¢
+4¢	+3¢	+2¢	+5¢	+2¢	+1¢
17¢	19¢	16¢	17¢	15¢	12¢

Write the missing addend.

19. 7 + _6_ = 13   **20.** _6_ + 4 = 10   **21.** 4 + _8_ = 12

22. 18 = 9 + _9_   **23.** 14 = _8_ + 6   **24.** 12 = 7 + _5_

25. 6 + _5_ = 11   **26.** _8_ + 7 = 15   **27.** 9 = 5 + _4_

28. _9_ + 1 = 10   **29.** 7 + _6_ = 13   **30.** _9_ + 3 = 12

31. 16 = _8_ + 8   **32.** 17 = 9 + _8_   **33.** 8 = 8 + _0_

Add: No Regrouping

Name _____

Date _____

$471 + 118 = \underline{?}$

Estimate.	Add the ones. $\longrightarrow$	Add the tens. $\longrightarrow$	Add the hundreds.

| | 471 | | +118 | | about 500 |

	h	t	o
	4	7	1
+	1	1	8
			9

	h	t	o
	4	7	1
+	1	1	8
		8	9

	h	t	o
	4	7	1
+	1	1	8
	5	8	9

Use front-end estimation to estimate. Then add.

1. 72
    +14
    86

2. 65
    +20
    85

3. 82
    +17
    99

4. 32
    +44
    76

5. 12
    +86
    98

6. 612
    +375
    987

7. 437
    +261
    698

8. 139
    +860
    999

9. 247
    +351
    598

10. 765
    +123
    888

Find the sum.

11.   24
    +201
    225

12. 336
    + 53
    389

13. 812
    + 16
    828

14.   39
    +520
    559

15.   70
    +219
    289

16. $6.17
    + 3.80
    $9.97

17. $2.48
    + 7.01
    $9.49

18. $4.24
    + 1.75
    $5.99

19. $5.37
    + 3.02
    $8.39

20. $8.11
    + 1.74
    $9.85

21. $24 + 75 = \underline{99}$

22. $81 + 607 = \underline{688}$

23. $936 + 23 = \underline{959}$

24. $\$0.17 + \$2.81 = \underline{\$2.99}$

25. $\$8.26 + \$1.42 = \underline{\$9.68}$

26. $\$5.74 + \$4.05 = \underline{\$9.79}$

27. $\$3.22 + \$2.35 = \underline{\$5.57}$

Estimate Sums

Name _____

Date _____

Round to the nearest:

ten	ten cents	hundred	dollar
49 $\longrightarrow$ 50	$.43 $\longrightarrow$ $.40	218 $\longrightarrow$ 200	$8.45 $\longrightarrow$ $8.00
+32 $\longrightarrow$ +30	+ .26 $\longrightarrow$ + .30	+159 $\longrightarrow$ +200	+ 7.55 $\longrightarrow$ + 8.00
about 80	about $.70	about 400	about $16.00

Estimate by rounding to the nearest ten or ten cents.

1.	56	60	2.	$.28	$.30	3.	$.32	$.30	4.	21	20
	13	10		.22	.20		.54	.50		46	50
	+18	+ 20		+ .31	+ .30		+ .09	+ .10		+38	+ 40
		90			$.80			$.90			110

5.	$.93	$.90	6.	$.56	$.60	7.	47	50	8.	244	240
	+ .22	+ .20		+ .48	+ .50		+63	+60		+ 27	+ 30
		$1.10			$1.10			110			270

Estimate by rounding to the nearest hundred or dollar.

9.	561	600	10.	821	800	11.	177	200	12.	752	800
	+213	+200		+137	+100		+346	+300		+395	+400
		800			900			500			1200

13.	727	700	14.	613	600	15.	271	300	16.	532	500
	+162	+200		+226	+200		+627	+600		+864	+900
		900			800			900			1400

17. $7.23 + $8.84　　　**18.** $6.15 + $2.36　　　**19.** $4.95 + $5.39

$7.00 + $9.00 = $16.00　　$6.00 + $2.00 = $8.00　　$5.00 + $5.00 = $10.00

Problem Solving Answers may vary.

20. A carton of milk costs $1.36 and a bunch of celery costs $.98. **About** how much do the two items cost?

$1.00 + $1.00 = $2.00; about $2.00

21. At the school play, the gym was filled with 232 parents and 57 students. **About** how many people came to the play?

230 + 60 = 290; about 290 people

Add with Regrouping

Name _____

Date _____

Estimate.

26 ⟶ 30
+18 ⟶ +20
about 50

Add.

tens	ones
¹2	6
+1	8
	4

tens	ones
¹2	6
+1	8
4	4

14 ones = 1 ten 4 ones

Estimate. Then find the sum. Accept reasonable estimates.

1. 16
   +17
   ‾33‾

2. 29
   +41
   ‾70‾

3. 64
   +26
   ‾90‾

4. 72
   +19
   ‾91‾

5. 48
   +36
   ‾84‾

6. 54
   +29
   ‾83‾

7. 38
   +58
   ‾96‾

8. 49
   +36
   ‾85‾

9. 28
   +52
   ‾80‾

10. 24
   +68
   ‾92‾

11. 14
   +45
   ‾59‾

12. 22
   + 7
   ‾29‾

13. 38
   +18
   ‾56‾

14. 36
   +57
   ‾93‾

15. 49
   +21
   ‾70‾

16. 67¢
   + 8¢
   ‾75¢‾

17. 29¢
   + 5¢
   ‾34¢‾

18. 47¢
   +27¢
   ‾74¢‾

19. 19¢
   +21¢
   ‾40¢‾

20. 14¢
   +68¢
   ‾82¢‾

Align and add.

21. 26 + 59 = __85__

22. 73 + 17 = __90__

23. 48 + 13 = __61__

24. 9¢ + 12¢ = __21¢__

25. 25¢ + 47¢ = __72¢__

26. 8¢ + 89¢ = __97¢__

Problem Solving

27. How many blue and green erasers are there in all?   24 + 17 = 41

28. Green and yellow?   17 + 18 = 35

29. Yellow and red?   18 + 19 = 37

30. Blue and yellow?   24 + 18 = 42

31. Green and red?   17 + 19 = 36

Erasers			
Blue	Green	Yellow	Red
24	17	18	19

Regroup Tens

Name _____

Date _____

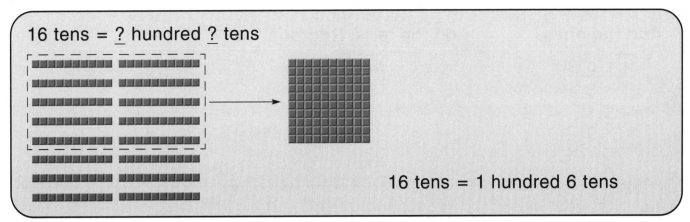

16 tens = ? hundred ? tens

16 tens = 1 hundred 6 tens

Regroup tens as hundreds and tens. You may use base ten blocks.

1. 14 tens =

    __1__ hundred __4__ tens

2. 17 tens =

    __1__ hundred __7__ tens

3. 25 tens =

    __2__ hundreds __5__ tens

4. 64 tens =

    __6__ hundreds __4__ tens

5. 32 tens =

    __3__ hundreds __2__ tens

6. 41 tens =

    __4__ hundreds __1__ ten

7. 50 tens =

    __5__ hundreds __0__ tens

8. 10 tens =

    __1__ hundred __0__ tens

9. 76 tens =

    __7__ hundreds __6__ tens

10. 83 tens =

    __8__ hundreds __3__ tens

11. 97 tens =

    __9__ hundreds __7__ tens

12. 28 tens =

    __2__ hundreds __8__ tens

13. 59 tens =

    __5__ hundreds __9__ tens

14. 44 tens =

    __4__ hundreds __4__ tens

15. 60 tens =

    __6__ hundreds __0__ tens

16. 80 tens =

    __8__ hundreds __0__ tens

Add: Regroup Tens

Name _____

Date _____

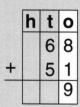

Add the ones.	Add the tens. Regroup.

h	t	o
	6	8
+	5	1
		9

h	t	o
	6	8
+	5	1
1	1	9

11 tens = 1 hundred 1 ten

Add.

1.	93 +34 127	2.	45 +82 127	3.	82 +37 119	4.	43 +65 108	5.	26 +81 107

6.	56 +71 127	7.	84 +45 129	8.	92 +22 114	9.	55 +83 138	10.	73 +35 108

11.	$.52 + .86 $1.38	12.	$.70 + .55 $1.25	13.	$.63 + .82 $1.45	14.	$.71 + .42 $1.13	15.	$.54 + .95 $1.49

16.	$.40 + .79 $1.19	17.	$.23 + .95 $1.18	18.	$.72 + .82 $1.54	19.	$.45 + .64 $1.09	20.	$.53 + .85 $1.38

21.	65 +82 147	22.	11 +98 109	23.	27 +90 117	24.	58 +71 129	25.	92 +83 175

Problem Solving

26. Charles collected 54 cans on Friday for the recycling drive. He collected 62 cans on Saturday. How many cans did he collect altogether?

$54 + 62 = 116$; 116 cans

Add: Regroup Twice

Name _____

Date _____

Add the ones. Regroup.	Add the tens. Regroup.

h	t	o
	¹	
	9	2
+	3	9
		1

11 ones = 1 ten 1 one

h	t	o
	¹	
	9	2
+	3	9
1	3	1

13 tens = 1 hundred 3 tens

Find the sum.

1. 99	2. 57	3. 63	4. 88	5. 45	6. 67
+34	+75	+39	+52	+65	+74
133	132	102	140	110	141

7. 78	8. 56	9. 47	10. 79	11. 58	12. 82
+24	+64	+58	+65	+47	+48
102	120	105	144	105	130

13. 64	14. 49	15. 72	16. 85	17. 45	18. 97
+38	+56	+68	+36	+59	+87
102	105	140	121	104	184

19. 44	20. 29	21. 88	22. 64	23. 46	24. 49
+56	+92	+76	+76	+57	+52
100	121	164	140	103	101

25. 86 + 57 = __143__   **26.** 48 + 79 = __127__   **27.** 55 + 67 = __122__

Problem Solving

28. Mr. Aoke ordered 56 picture books and 58 poetry books for the Wise Owl book store. How many books did he order altogether?

__56 + 58 = 114; 114 books__

29. Use the digits ③, ⑤, ⑨, and ④ only once to make 2 addends whose sum is between 100 and 110.

__59 and 43 or 49 and 53; 102__

Three-Digit Addition; More Regrouping in Addition

Name _____

Date _____

Estimate.   **Add.**

$$425 \rightarrow 400$$
$$+188 \rightarrow +200$$
about 600

h	t	o
4	2¹	5
+ 1	8	8
		3

13 ones =
1 ten 3 ones

h	t	o
4¹	2¹	5
+ 1	8	8
	1	3

11 ones =
1 hundred 1 ten

h	t	o
4¹	2¹	5
+ 1	8	8
6	1	3

Estimate. Then add.

1. 123
   +139
   262

2. 397
   + 45
   442

3. 132
   +184
   316

4. 576
   +136
   712

5. 273
   +472
   745

6. 257
   +136
   393

7. 274
   +253
   527

8. 398
   +375
   773

9. 192
   +239
   431

10. 388
   +162
   550

11. $2.26
   + 2.18
   $4.44

12. $1.96
   + .95
   $2.91

13. $3.54
   + 2.73
   $6.27

14. $1.46
   + 3.96
   $5.42

15. $4.87
   + 3.75
   $8.62

16. 345
   +185
   530

17. 627
   +297
   924

18. 304
   +206
   510

19. 366
   +359
   725

20. 806
   + 84
   890

Align and add.

21. 938 + 52 = ___990___

22. 46 + 265 = ___311___

23. 474 + 317 = ___791___

24. 731 + 169 = ___990___

25. 573 + 238 = ___811___

26. 419 + 478 = ___897___

Problem Solving

27. Find the total of 446 first-class stamps and 473 airmail stamps.

___446 + 473 = 919; 919 stamps___

Mental Math

Name _____

Date _____

Break apart numbers to find tens.	For more than two addends look for tens or one hundred.
$32 + 47 = \underline{?}$ Think: $(30 + 2) + (40 + 7)$ $(30 + 40) + (2 + 7)$ $70 + 9 = 79$	$28 + 42 + 26 = \underline{?}$ $70 \quad + 26 = 96$

Add mentally.

1. $16 + 6 = \underline{\ 22\ }$ **2.** $26 + 6 = \underline{\ 32\ }$ **3.** $36 + 6 = \underline{\ 42\ }$

4. $25 + 9 = \underline{\ 34\ }$ **5.** $35 + 9 = \underline{\ 44\ }$ **6.** $45 + 9 = \underline{\ 54\ }$

7. $57 + 8 = \underline{\ 65\ }$ **8.** $74 + 7 = \underline{\ 81\ }$ **9.** $93 + 8 = \underline{\ 101\ }$

10. $57 + 6 + 14 = \underline{\ 77\ }$ **11.** $13 + 9 + 47 = \underline{\ 69\ }$

12. $26 + 9 + 21 = \underline{\ 56\ }$ **13.** $64 + 15 + 16 = \underline{\ 95\ }$

14. $34 + 44 + 9 = \underline{\ 87\ }$ **15.** $42 + 34 + 22 = \underline{\ 98\ }$

	16.	17.	18.	19.	20.
	19 +32 ‾‾‾ 51	44 +61 ‾‾‾ 105	57 +25 ‾‾‾ 82	71 +16 ‾‾‾ 87	56 +61 ‾‾‾ 117

	21.	22.	23.	24.	25.
	14 26 +42 ‾‾‾ 82	33 38 +27 ‾‾‾ 98	26 45 +14 ‾‾‾ 85	29 49 +71 ‾‾‾ 149	46 18 +34 ‾‾‾ 98

Problem Solving

26. Kathleen had 24 glass birds in her collection. For her birthday, she received 37 more glass birds. How many glass birds does Kathleen have now?

$24 + 37 = 61$; 61 glass birds

21

Regroup Hundreds as Thousands

Name _____

Date _____

> **Regroup.**
>
> 1 thousand 12 hundreds =   23 hundreds =
>   ☐2☐ thousands ☐2☐ hundreds   ☐2☐ thousands ☐3☐ hundreds

Regroup.

1. 15 hundreds =

  __1__ thousand __5__ hundreds

2. 19 hundreds =

  __1__ thousand __9__ hundreds

3. 12 hundreds =

  __1__ thousand __2__ hundreds

4. 73 hundreds =

  __7__ thousands __3__ hundreds

5. 28 hundreds =

  __2__ thousands __8__ hundreds

6. 8 thousands 16 hundreds =

  __9__ thousands __6__ hundreds

7. 4 thousands 12 hundreds =

  __5__ thousands __2__ hundreds

8. 3 thousands 14 hundreds =

  __4__ thousands __4__ hundreds

9. 3 thousands 34 hundreds =

  __6__ thousands __4__ hundreds

10. 5 thousands 36 hundreds =

  __8__ thousands __6__ hundreds

Match.

11. 6 thousands 38 hundreds = __d__

12. 2 thousands 23 hundreds = __c__

13. 4 thousands 18 hundreds = __e__

14. 3 thousands 44 hundreds = __a__

15. 7 thousands 16 hundreds = __b__

16. 5 thousands 45 hundreds = __f__

a) 7 thousands 4 hundreds

b) 8 thousands 6 hundreds

c) 4 thousands 3 hundreds

d) 9 thousands 8 hundreds

e) 5 thousands 8 hundreds

f) 9 thousands 5 hundreds

Three or More Addends

Name _____

Date _____

Estimate.   Add.

$4.22 ⟶ $4.00
4.54 ⟶ 5.00
+ 2.36 ⟶ + 2.00
about $11.00

```
  1
$4.2 2
 4.5 4
+ 2.3 6
      2
```

```
 1   1
$4.2 2
 4.5 4
+ 2.3 6
    1 2
```

```
 1   1
$4.2 2
 4.5 4
+ 2.3 6
$11.1 2
```

Estimate. Then add. Accept reasonable estimates.

1.	2.	3.	4.	5.
249	421	472	739	173
344	178	249	73	271
+423	+465	+256	+164	+ 18
1016	1064	977	976	462

6.	7.	8.	9.	10.
123	217	$3.80	$4.92	$5.69
526	324	1.25	2.79	3.34
+136	+645	+ 5.55	+ 7.21	+ 9.53
785	1186	$10.60	$14.92	$18.56

Find the sum.

11.	12.	13.	14.	15.
123	221	233	616	429
247	419	344	117	772
423	320	602	201	533
+145	+180	+182	+383	+155
938	1140	1361	1317	1889

Grapes $1.15	Meat Pie $3.25	Bread $2.49	Apples $2.10	Oranges $3.85

Use the pictures to find the total cost for each.

16. orange, apples, and grapes $3.85 + $2.10 + $1.15 = $7.10; $7.10

17. bread, meat pie, and oranges $2.49 + $3.25 + $3.85 = $9.59; $9.59

18. meat pie, grapes, bread, and apples $3.25 + $1.15 + $2.49 + $2.10 = $8.99; $8.99

19. oranges, grapes, meat pie, and apples $3.85 + $1.15 + $3.25 + $2.10 = $10.35; $10.35

20. bread, apples, meat pie, and oranges $2.49 + $2.10 + $3.25 + $3.85 = $11.69; $11.69

Add Larger Numbers

Name _____

Date _____

Estimate.	Add.	th	h	t	o		th	h	t	o		th	h	t	o		th	h	t	o
5627 → 6000				1					1	1			1	1	1			1	1	1
+2394 → +2000		5	6	2	7		5	6	2	7		5	6	2	7		5	6	2	7
about 8000		+2	3	9	4		+2	3	9	4		+2	3	9	4		+2	3	9	4
					1				2	1			0	2	1		8	0	2	1

Estimate. Then add. Accept reasonable estimates.

1.	3768	2.	2492	3.	1986	4.	5345	5.	5098
	+2986		+ 639		+7123		+ 985		+ 109
	6754		3131		9109		6330		5207

6.	2985	7.	1357	8.	4930	9.	2794	10.	3850
	+1328		+5456		+2109		+5739		+2465
	4313		6813		7039		8533		6315

Find the sum. Use the $ and . when needed.

11.	2552	12.	1678	13.	4433	14.	$18.60	15.	$44.41
	+ 331		+ 848		+ 48		+ 5.62		+ .71
	2883		2526		4481		$24.22		$45.12

16.	2929	17.	1829	18.	$33.32	19.	$24.21	20.	$45.37
	+6363		+3453		+ 56.74		+ 47.32		+ 13.26
	9292		5282		$90.06		$71.53		$58.63

21. 2537 + 1236 = __3773__

22. 1483 + 8263 = __9746__

23. 3839 + 4375 = __8214__

24. $6.48 + $55.66 = __$62.14__

25. $29.87 + $9.79 = __$39.66__

26. $59.86 + $36.59 = __$96.45__

Problem Solving

27. Monday morning, 2466 cars crossed the bridge to the city. During the rest of the day, 3254 more cars crossed the bridge. How many cars crossed the bridge on Monday in all?

2466 + 3254 = 5720; 5720 cars

Problem-Solving Strategy: Use Simpler Numbers

Name _____

Date _____

> Joe and Fred need 876 bricks to build a chimney.
> They also need 327 more to build the fireplace.
> How many bricks do they need?
> **Use simpler numbers.** Use 80 for 876 and use 30 for 327.
> **Add:** 80 + 30 = 110 Now compute the numbers in the problem.
> Joe and Fred need to buy 1203 bricks.
>
> $\begin{array}{r} \scriptstyle 1\ 1 \\ 876 \\ +327 \\ \hline 1203 \end{array}$

Solve. Do your work on a separate sheet of paper.

1. Joe counted three bundles of boards. One had 276 boards, another had 319, and the third had 121. How many boards were in the three bundles in all?

   276 + 319 + 121 = 716;
   716 boards

2. Fred paid $75.50 for house plans, $9.75 for a hammer, and $13.50 for a saw. How much did these items cost altogether?

   $75.50 + $9.75 + $13.50 = $98.75;
   $98.75

3. Each side of a house needed a different amount of siding. The front needed 248 feet and the back needed 288 feet. The sides needed 450 and 420 feet. How many feet were needed in all?

   248 + 288 + 450 + 420 = 1406;
   1406 feet

4. Fred wanted wood floors in the house. He needed 578 feet of wood flooring upstairs and 725 feet downstairs. What was the total number of feet of wood flooring that he needed?

   578 + 725 = 1303; 1303 feet

5. Joe used 3 spools of wire for the electricity. Each spool had 250 feet. How many feet of wire were used?

   250 + 250 + 250 = 750; 750 feet

6. The roof needed 140 shingles on one side and 185 on the other. How many shingles did Joe need to buy?

   140 + 185 = 325; 325 shingles

7. Joe insulated a house. The walls needed 565 yards of insulation and the roof needed 378 yards. How many yards did Joe have to buy?

   565 + 378 = 943; 943 yards

8. A house that Joe and Fred were building called for 137 long studs and 98 short studs. How many studs did they need to buy?

   137 + 98 = 235; 235 studs

Problem-Solving Applications: Mixed Review

Name _____

Date _____

Solve each problem and explain the method you used. If needed, do all your work on a separate sheet of paper.

Read ▸ Plan ▸ Solve ▸ Check

Strategy File

Use These Strategies
Guess and Test
Find a Pattern
Draw a Picture
Make a Table
Use More Than One Step
Use Simpler Numbers

1. Sean's mother spent $52.25 on his shoes and $68.43 on his sister Fiona's shoes. How much did Sean's mother spend in all?

   $52.25 + $68.43 = $120.68; $120.68

2. Jack had 645 baseball cards. He bought 50 cards in April and 10 less cards in May than in April. How many cards does Jack have now?

   645 + 50 = 695; 50 − 10 = 40;
   695 + 40 = 735; 735 cards

3. 2,363 people were at Lisa's graduation. 3,166 people were at Melissa's graduation. How many people watched Lisa and Melissa graduate in all?

   2,363 + 3,166 = 5,529; 5,529 people

4. Randy spent $436 on a stereo and $294 on a tv. Paula spent $100 on a radio. How much more than Paula did Randy spend?

   $436 + $294 = $730;
   $730 − $100 = $630; $630

5. It is 862 ft from John's house to Maria's. It is 129 ft further to Flo's house. How far is it from John's house to Flo's house?

   862 + 129 = 991; 991 ft

6. Each day Ashley practices free throws. The first day she takes 12 shots, and every day after she takes 2 more than the previous day. How many free throws will she shoot on the 6th day?

   22

7. Kristin drove 328 miles on Friday, 262 miles on Saturday, and 233 miles on Sunday. How many miles did she drive total?

   328 + 262 + 233 = 823; 823 miles

8. Jeffrey's Grove Elementary School has 1217 students. Lynn Elementary has 1322 students. How many students go to the two schools in all?

   1217 + 1322 = 2539; 2539 students

9. There are 36 fans at the Hawks/Bulldogs basketball game. Every third fan is cheering for the Hawks. How many fans are cheering for the Bulldogs?

   12 fans

Subtraction Concepts

Name _____

Date _____

- Sam had 21 toys.
  He gave away 3 toys.
  How many are left?

  Take Away
  21 – 3 = 18
  Eighteen toys are left.

- There are 21 toys.
  Eleven are stuffed animals.
  How many are not stuffed animals?

  Find Part of a Whole Set
  21 – 11 = 10
  10 are not stuffed animals.

- Sam had 21 toys.
  Grace had 39 toys.
  How many more toys did
  Grace have?

  Compare
  39 – 21 = 18
  Grace had 18 more toys.

- Grace has $16. She needs $29.
  How many more dollars
  does she need?

  Find How Many More Are Needed
  $29 – $16 = $13
  She needs $13 more.

Problem Solving

Write which meaning of subtraction you used.

1. The Pretty Pooch Pet Store had 68 beagles.
   They sold 12 beagles. How many beagles
   were left?

   68 – 12 = 56; 56 beagles;
   Take Away

2. Jack collects animal stamps. He can fit
   45 stamps in an album. He has 32 stamps.
   How many more does he need to fill the
   album?

   45 – 32 = 13; 13 more stamps;
   Find how Many More Are Needed

3. Miko has 22 tropical fish. Alex has 10 fish.
   How many more fish does Miko have?

   22 – 10 = 12; 12 more;
   Compare

4. Anna wants to buy a book about cats that
   costs $28. She has $18. How much more
   money does she need?

   $28 – $18 = $10; $10 more;
   Find how Many More Are Needed

5. There are 46 kittens at the pet store.
   15 kittens are gray. How many kittens
   are not gray?

   46 – 15 = 31; 31 are not gray;
   Part of a Whole Set

 27

Subtract: No Regrouping

Name _____

Date _____

Estimate.

Use front-end estimation.

$$283 \longrightarrow 200$$
$$-121 \longrightarrow -100$$
$$\text{about } 100$$

Subtract.

h	t	o
2	8	3
−1	2	1
		2

h	t	o
2	8	3
−1	2	1
	6	2

h	t	o
2	8	3
−1	2	1
1	6	2

Use front-end digits to estimate. Then find the difference.

1. 355
    − 33
    322

2. 648
    − 23
    625

3. 529
    − 27
    502

4. 862
    −761
    101

5. 365
    − 21
    344

6. 286
    − 24
    262

7. $1.68
    − .53
    $1.15

8. $5.76
    − .41
    $5.35

9. $.95
    − .65
    $.30

10. $7.19
    − 2.16
    $5.03

11. 57¢
    − 20¢
    37¢

12. $8.92
    − 4.51
    $4.41

Subtract.

13. 289
    −224
    65

14. 742
    −231
    511

15. 768
    −243
    525

16. 356
    − 51
    305

17. 597
    −185
    412

18. $4.29
    − 1.15
    $3.14

19. $8.65
    − 8.32
    $0.33

20. $4.59
    − 2.45
    $2.14

21. $6.75
    − 3.71
    $3.04

22. $9.86
    − 5.43
    $4.43

Align and subtract.

23. 472 − 70
    472
    − 70
    402

24. 581 − 281
    581
    −281
    300

25. $4.21 − $4.11
    $4.21
    − 4.11
    $0.10

26. $2.34 − $.21
    $2.34
    − .21
    $2.13

27. $3.56 − $.33
    $3.56
    − .33
    $3.23

28. 658 − 232
    658
    −232
    426

Estimate Differences

Round to the nearest:

ten	hundred	ten cents	dollar
55 → 60	838 → 800	$.77 → $.80	$18.75 → $19
−24 → −20	−269 → −300	− .23 → − .20	− 5.12 → − 5
40	500	$.60	$14

Estimate by rounding to the nearest ten or ten cents.

1. 67 70
  −12 −10
     60

2. 65 70
  −32 −30
     40

3. 73 70
  −15 −20
     50

4. 60 60
  −48 −50
     10

5. $.25 $.30
  − .11 − .10
     $.20

6. $2.59 $2.60
  − .19 − .20
     $2.40

7. $.46 $.50
  − .31 − .30
     $.20

8. $2.75 $2.80
  − 1.28 − 1.30
     $1.50

9. 78 − 37 ___40___

10. 51 − 39 ___10___

11. $3.34 − $1.28 ___$2___

Estimate by rounding to the nearest hundred or dollar.

12. 259 300
  −112 −100
     200

13. 598 600
  −192 −200
     400

14. 646 600
  −231 −200
     400

15. 388 400
  −131 −100
     300

16. $3.72 − $1.24 ___$3.00___

17. $65.46 − $22.20 ___$43.00___

Problem Solving Estimates may vary.

18. During one hour at the airport, $876 was taken in from food sales. The next hour, $564 was collected. **About** how much less was collected during the second hour?

$900 − $600 = $300;
about $300 less

19. Billy sold his bike for $159.43. He spent $118.07 on a new bike. **About** how much money does Billy have left?

$159 − $118 = $41;
about $41 left

Subtract with Regrouping

Name _____

Date _____

Estimate by rounding.

$$44 \longrightarrow 40$$
$$-18 \longrightarrow -20$$
$$\text{about } 20$$

Subtract. Regroup as needed.

tens	ones
³4̸	¹⁴4̸
− 1	8
	6

tens	ones
³4̸	¹⁴4̸
− 1	8
2	6

4 tens 4 ones = 3 tens 14 ones

Estimate by rounding. Then find the difference. Accept reasonable estimates.

1.
$$85$$
$$-26$$
$$59$$

2.
$$92$$
$$-36$$
$$56$$

3.
$$65$$
$$-28$$
$$37$$

4.
$$43$$
$$-26$$
$$17$$

5.
$$72$$
$$-35$$
$$37$$

6.
$$56$$
$$-48$$
$$8$$

7.
$$24$$
$$-18$$
$$6$$

8.
$$47$$
$$-39$$
$$8$$

9.
$$83$$
$$-46$$
$$37$$

10.
$$74$$
$$-29$$
$$45$$

11.
$$56$$
$$-\ 8$$
$$48$$

12.
$$94$$
$$-38$$
$$56$$

Align and subtract.

13. 62 − 24
$$62$$
$$-24$$
$$38$$

14. 70¢ − 52¢
$$70¢$$
$$-52¢$$
$$18¢$$

15. $.68 − $.19
$$\$.68$$
$$-\ .19$$
$$\$.49$$

16. 45 − 36
$$45$$
$$-36$$
$$9$$

17. 55¢ − 37¢
$$55¢$$
$$-37¢$$
$$18¢$$

18. $.75 − $.36
$$\$.75$$
$$-\ .36$$
$$\$.39$$

19. $.72 − $.57
$$\$.72$$
$$-\ .57$$
$$\$.15$$

20. 63¢ − 29¢
$$63¢$$
$$-29¢$$
$$34¢$$

21. 78 − 49
$$78$$
$$-49$$
$$29$$

Problem Solving

22. Randall had 42 stickers. He gave some away. Then he had 27 left. How many did he give away?

42 − 27 = 15; 15 stickers

Regroup
Hundreds and Dollars

Name _____

Date _____

6 hundreds 8 tens =	7 dollars 3 dimes =
5 hundreds + 1 hundred + 8 tens =	6 dollars + 1 dollar + 3 dimes =
5 hundreds + 10 tens + 8 tens =	6 dollars + 10 dimes + 3 dimes =
5 hundreds + 18 tens =	6 dollars + 13 dimes =
5 hundreds 18 tens	6 dollars 13 dimes

Regroup. Use base ten blocks and play money to help.

1. 7 hundreds 2 tens =

_6_ hundreds _12_ tens

2. 3 hundreds 4 tens =

_2_ hundreds _14_ tens

3. 2 hundreds 0 tens =

_1_ hundred _10_ tens

4. 9 hundreds 3 tens =

_8_ hundreds _13_ tens

5. 8 hundreds 8 tens =

_7_ hundreds _18_ tens

6. 4 hundreds 5 tens =

_3_ hundreds _15_ tens

7. 9 hundreds 1 ten =

_8_ hundreds _11_ tens

8. 7 hundreds 7 tens =

_6_ hundreds _17_ tens

9. 1 dollar 1 dime =

_0_ dollars _11_ dimes

10. 6 dollars 1 dime =

_5_ dollars _11_ dimes

11. 5 dollars 0 dimes =

_4_ dollars _10_ dimes

12. 3 dollars 2 dimes =

_2_ dollars _12_ dimes

13. 8 dollars 6 dimes =

_7_ dollars _16_ dimes

14. 4 dollars 4 dimes =

_3_ dollars _14_ dimes

15. 2 dollars 2 dimes =

_1_ dollar _12_ dimes

16. 5 dollars 8 dimes =

_4_ dollars _18_ dimes

17. 6 hundreds 7 tens = _5_ hundreds _17_ tens

Regroup Once in Subtraction

Name _____

Date _____

Estimate by rounding.

328 → 300
−182 → −200
about 100

Subtract. Regroup as needed.

h	t	o
3	2	8
−1	8	2
		6

h	t	o
²3̸	¹²2	8
−1	8	2
	4	6

h	t	o
²3̸	¹²2	8
−1	8	2
1	4	6

Estimate by rounding. Then subtract. Accept reasonable estimates.

1. 417
   −153
    264

2. 239
   −184
     55

3. 927
   −435
    492

4. 179
   − 84
     95

5. 878
   −296
    582

6. 765
   −273
    492

7. 349
   −157
    192

8. 567
   − 87
    480

9. 454
   −162
    292

10. 238
    − 65
     173

11. 375
    −126
     249

12. 945
    −372
     573

13. 186
    − 93
     93

14. 284
    −116
     168

15. 416
    −107
     309

16. $2.35
    − 1.41
    $ .94

17. $6.78
    − 4.29
    $2.49

18. $3.86
    − .94
    $2.92

19. $3.15
    − 1.22
    $1.93

20. $8.88
    − 7.95
    $ .93

Align and subtract.

21. 397 − 148
```
 397
−148
 249
```

22. 276 − 81
```
 276
− 81
 195
```

23. 756 − 273
```
 756
−273
 483
```

24. 476 − 388
```
 476
−388
  88
```

25. 989 − 899
```
 989
−899
  90
```

26. 678 − 592
```
 678
−592
  86
```

27. $6.18 − $.31
```
$6.18
−  .31
$5.87
```

28. $7.11 − $2.80
```
$7.11
− 2.80
$4.31
```

29. $5.25 − $1.31
```
$5.25
− 1.31
$3.94
```

30. $6.18 − $3.43
```
$6.18
− 3.43
$2.75
```

Regroup Twice in Subtraction

Name _____

Date _____

Estimate by rounding.

873 ⟶ 900
−587 ⟶ −600
about 300

Subtract.

h	t	o
	6	13
8	7̸	3̸
−5	8	7
		6

h	t	o
	16	
7	6̸	13
8̸	7̸	3̸
−5	8	7
	8	6

h	t	o
	16	
7	6̸	13
8̸	7̸	3̸
−5	8	7
2	8	6

Estimate by rounding. Then subtract.

1. 750 −393 357 **2.** 322 −228 94 **3.** 854 −276 578 **4.** 763 −185 578 **5.** 621 −182 439

6. 567 −198 369 **7.** 478 −279 199 **8.** 581 − 96 485 **9.** 555 − 76 479 **10.** 911 −483 428

11. 931 −375 556 **12.** 423 −128 295 **13.** $6.73 − 4.87 $1.86 **14.** $4.78 − 3.99 $ .79 **15.** $6.17 − 1.28 $4.89

Align and subtract.

16. 715 − 236   715 −236 479

17. 853 − 284   853 −284 569

18. 691 − 398   691 −398 293

19. $7.88 − $2.89 $7.88 − 2.89 $4.99

20. $9.64 − $3.86 $9.64 − 3.86 $5.78

Problem Solving

21. How much change will Tom receive if he spends $3.47 and gives the clerk a five-dollar bill and 2 quarters?

$5.00 + $.25 + $.25 = $5.50
$5.50 − $3.47 = $2.03

Use with Lesson 3-7, text pages 112–113. Copyright © William H. Sadlier, Inc. All rights reserved. 33

Regroup with Zeros

Name _____

Date _____

Estimate by rounding.

$$500 \longrightarrow 500$$
$$-379 \longrightarrow -400$$
about 100

Subtract. Regroup as needed.

h	t	o
4	10	
5̶	0̶	0
3	7	9

h	t	o
	9	
4	1̶0	10
5̶	0̶	0̶
3	7	9

h	t	o
	9	
4	1̶0	10
5̶	0̶	0̶
3	7	9
1	2	1

Estimate by rounding. Then subtract. Accept reasonable estimates.

1. 400
   −118
   ‾‾‾‾
    282

2. 300
   −225
   ‾‾‾‾
     75

3. 700
   −346
   ‾‾‾‾
    354

4. 300
   −107
   ‾‾‾‾
    193

5. 700
   −128
   ‾‾‾‾
    572

6. 500
   −257
   ‾‾‾‾
    243

7. 800
   −424
   ‾‾‾‾
    376

8. 600
   −305
   ‾‾‾‾
    295

9. 400
   −277
   ‾‾‾‾
    123

10. 300
    −198
    ‾‾‾‾
     102

11. 100
    − 75
    ‾‾‾‾
      25

12. 200
    − 28
    ‾‾‾‾
     172

13. $9.00
    − 5.19
    ‾‾‾‾‾
    $3.81

14. $4.00
    − 1.18
    ‾‾‾‾‾
    $2.82

15. $3.00
    − 2.25
    ‾‾‾‾‾
    $ .75

16. $7.00
    − 5.55
    ‾‾‾‾‾
    $1.45

Align and subtract.

17. 900 − 575   900
                 −575
                 ‾‾‾‾
                  325

18. 500 − 275   500
                 −275
                 ‾‾‾‾
                  225

19. $6.00 − $1.49 $6.00
                     − 1.49
                     ‾‾‾‾‾
                     $4.51

20. 206 − 118   206
                 −118
                 ‾‾‾‾
                   88

21. 808 − 239   808
                 −239
                 ‾‾‾‾
                  569

22. $5.02 − $2.23 $5.02
                     − 2.23
                     ‾‾‾‾‾
                     $2.79

Problem Solving

23. The video store has 800 movies to rent. One weekend, all but 298 movies were rented. How many movies were rented that weekend?

$800 − 298 = 502$; 502 movies

Regroup Thousands as Hundreds

Name _____

Date _____

> 2 thousands 4 hundreds = 1 thousand + 1 thousand + 4 hundreds
> = 1 thousand + 10 hundreds + 4 hundreds
> = 1 thousand + 14 hundreds
> = 1 thousand 14 hundreds

Regroup 1 thousand as 10 hundreds.
Write how many thousands and hundreds.

1. 3 thousands 7 hundreds =

___2___ thousands ___17___ hundreds

2. 6 thousands 4 hundreds =

___5___ thousands ___14___ hundreds

3. 1 thousand 6 hundreds =

___0___ thousands ___16___ hundreds

4. 5 thousands 5 hundreds =

___4___ thousands ___15___ hundreds

5. 8 thousands 1 hundred =

___7___ thousands ___11___ hundreds

6. 3 thousands 2 hundreds =

___2___ thousands ___12___ hundreds

7. 9 thousands 6 hundreds =

___8___ thousands ___16___ hundreds

8. 7 thousands =

___6___ thousands ___10___ hundreds

9. 4 thousands =

___3___ thousands ___10___ hundreds

10. 3 thousands 2 hundreds =

___2___ thousands ___12___ hundreds

11. 2 thousands 8 hundred =

___1___ thousand ___18___ hundred

12. 8 thousands =

___7___ thousands ___10___ hundreds

13. 7 thousands 6 hundreds =

___6___ thousands ___16___ hundreds

14. 6 thousands 2 hundreds =

___5___ thousands ___12___ hundreds

Subtract Larger Numbers

Name _____

Date _____

$7022 - 5974 = \underline{?}$

th	h	t	o
7	0	2 (1)	2 (12)
-5	9	7	4
			8

th	h	t	o
7̶ (6)	0̶ (9,10)	2̶ (11,X)	2 (12)
-5	9	7	4
		4	8

th	h	t	o
7̶ (6)	0̶ (9,10)	2̶ (11,X)	2 (12)
-5	9	7	4
	0	4	8

th	h	t	o
7̶ (6)	0̶ (9,10)	2̶ (11,X)	2 (12)
-5	9	7	4
1	0	4	8

Check
```
  1048
+ 5974
  7022
```

Estimate by rounding. Then subtract. Accept reasonable estimates.

1. 5762
   −1814
   3948

2. 3057
   − 832
   2225

3. 7582
   −2816
   4766

4. 6005
   −2316
   3689

5. 8000
   −2143
   5857

6. 2876
   − 951
   1925

7. 5000
   −1638
   3362

8. 8736
   −6495
   2241

9. $20.00
   − 4.53
   $15.47

10. $63.95
   − 8.94
   $55.01

11. $76.85
   − 38.69
   $38.16

12. $50.00
   − 28.59
   $21.41

13. $78.95
   − 34.26
   $44.69

Subtract. Then check by addition.

14. 3789   Check: 2544
    −1245   +1245
     2544   3789

15. 5010   Check: 2920
    −2090   +2090
     2920   5010

16. 4201   Check: 3172
    −1029   +1029
     3172   4201

17. 7543   Check: 2417
    −5126   +5126
     2417   7543

18. $89.56   Check: $52.28
    − 37.28   + 37.28
    $52.28 $89.56

19. $59.57   Check: $26.73
    − 32.84   + 32.84
    $26.73 $59.57

Problem Solving

20. Arnold buys a DVD for $17.45. He has two $10 bills and a $5 bill. Which two bills should Arnold give the cashier? What change can Arnold receive?

$10 + $10 = $20; $20 > $17.45;
$20 − $17.45 = $2.45
two $10 bills; $2.45

Choose a Computation Method

Name _____

Date _____

Subtract: 675 – 300
- Can you subtract mentally? Use mental math.
- Are the numbers too large to subtract mentally? Use paper and pencil.

$$\begin{array}{r} 675 \\ -300 \\ \hline 375 \end{array}$$

Subtract. Use mental math or pencil and paper.

1.
$$\begin{array}{r} 286 \\ -120 \\ \hline 166 \end{array}$$

2.
$$\begin{array}{r} 900 \\ -600 \\ \hline 300 \end{array}$$

3.
$$\begin{array}{r} 342 \\ -227 \\ \hline 115 \end{array}$$

4.
$$\begin{array}{r} 250 \\ -138 \\ \hline 112 \end{array}$$

5.
$$\begin{array}{r} \$2.99 \\ -\ 1.10 \\ \hline \$1.89 \end{array}$$

6.
$$\begin{array}{r} 250 \\ -200 \\ \hline 50 \end{array}$$

7.
$$\begin{array}{r} 600 \\ -457 \\ \hline 143 \end{array}$$

8.
$$\begin{array}{r} \$4.95 \\ -\ 3.50 \\ \hline \$1.45 \end{array}$$

9.
$$\begin{array}{r} \$2.38 \\ -\ .38 \\ \hline \$2.00 \end{array}$$

10.
$$\begin{array}{r} \$8.50 \\ -\ 5.26 \\ \hline \$3.24 \end{array}$$

11.
$$\begin{array}{r} 913 \\ -285 \\ \hline 628 \end{array}$$

12.
$$\begin{array}{r} 4000 \\ -1000 \\ \hline 3000 \end{array}$$

13.
$$\begin{array}{r} 6056 \\ -4059 \\ \hline 1997 \end{array}$$

14.
$$\begin{array}{r} \$9.77 \\ -\ 5.01 \\ \hline \$4.76 \end{array}$$

15.
$$\begin{array}{r} \$1.75 \\ -\ .25 \\ \hline \$1.50 \end{array}$$

Problem Solving

16. Louise sold 738 hot dogs at her restaurant this month. She expects to sell 100 less next month than she did this month. How many hot dogs does Louise expect to sell?

738 – 100 = 638; 638 hot dogs

17. Troy bought a used car for $9300. Enrique bought a used car for $7200. How much more was Troy's car than Enrique's car?

$9300 – $7200 = $2100; $2100 more

18. Rodestraat's Christmas tree has 7000 lights on it. If 1248 bulbs need to be replaced, how many don't need to be replaced?

7000 – 1248 = 5752; 5752 bulbs

 37

Problem-Solving Strategy: Choose the Operation

Name _____

Date _____

> Jed bought a window box for $12.75, a flower pot for $7.95, and a hanging planter for $16.30. How much did Jed spend?
>
> Jed spent $37.00
>
> Think: Add $12.75 + $7.95 + $16.30
>
> $12.75
> 7.95
> + 16.30
> $37.00

Solve. Do your work on a separate sheet of paper.

1. The garden store's bulb bins contain 237 tulip bulbs, 466 daffodil bulbs, and 719 crocus bulbs. How many bulbs are there in all?

   237 + 466 + 719 = 1422;
   1422 bulbs

2. Carroll wants to fence in his flower bed. He needs 1246 feet of fencing. The store has 1098 feet in stock. How much more fencing does Carroll need?

   1246 − 1098 = 148; 148 feet

3. At the end of the week, there were 485 3-inch peat pots left in the store. At the beginning of the week, there had been 2390 pots. How many pots were sold that week?

   2390 − 485 = 1905; 1905 pots

4. Arnie wants to plant a new lawn. A grass rake costs $17.44, hay mulch costs $14.60, and 25 pounds of grass seed costs $45.19. How much will it cost Arnie to plant a lawn?

   $17.44 + $14.60 + $45.19 = $77.23; $77.23

5. Aretha worked 32 hours, 30 hours, and 29 hours during three weeks in June. How many hours did she work altogether?

   32 + 30 + 29 = 91; 91 hours

6. Electric hedge clippers cost $33.72. A rotary lawn mower costs $85.95. How much more expensive is the rotary mower?

   $85.95 − $33.72 = $52.23; $52.23

7. Evita buys a window box for $10.99. She also buys plants that cost $14.50. How much does she spend?

   $10.99 + $14.50 = $25.49; $25.49

8. Luis sold 958 packets of seeds. Jack sold 1322 packets. How many more packets did Jack sell than Luis?

   1322 − 958 = 364; 364 packets

Problem-Solving Applications: Mixed Review

Solve each problem and explain the method you used. If needed, do all your work on a separate sheet of paper.

Read ▶ Plan ▶ Solve ▶ Check

Strategy File

Use These Strategies
Choose the Operation
Use Simpler Numbers
Draw a Picture
Make a Table
Guess and Test
Use More Than One Step

1. 37 students play soccer for Cary Academy. 24 play on the varsity team and the rest play on the Junior Varsity team. How many students play on the Junior Varsity soccer team?

   37 − 24 = 13; 13 students

2. Leo bought a harmonica with a 10-dollar bill. He received $2.63 in change. How much did the harmonica cost?

   $10.00 − $2.63 = $7.37; $7.37

3. Horatio is saving for a soccer ball that costs $21.50. He has already saved $16.25. How much more money does he need to save?

   $21.50 − $16.25 = $5.25; $5.25

4. Lauren ran twice as many laps as Annie. Combined they ran 24 laps. How many laps did Annie run?

   8 × 2 = 16; 16 + 8 = 24; 8 laps

5. A train ticket usually costs $12.00. If Rodney pays $2.70 less than that, how much did his ticket cost?

   $12.00 − $2.70 = $9.30; $9.30

6. Kenneth is collecting Red Cross donations. The first person gave him $2.10, the second $2.20, the third $2.30, and so on. If this rate continues, how much will the eighth person donate?

   $2.80

7. Maureen wants to study for 300 minutes this week. She studied 45 minutes Monday, 62 minutes Tuesday, and 72 minutes Wednesday. How much must she study the rest of the week to reach her goal?

   45 + 62 + 72 = 179;
   300 − 179 = 121; 121 minutes

8. The New York Stars have 8000 hats to give away before a game. If they have 2256 hats at the end of the game, how many hats did they give away?

   8000 − 2256 = 5744; 5744 hats

9. William wants to buy an mp3 player. The one he wants costs $345.00. He has $255.25. How much more money does he need?

   $345.00 − $255.25 = $89.75; $89.75

Understand Multiplication

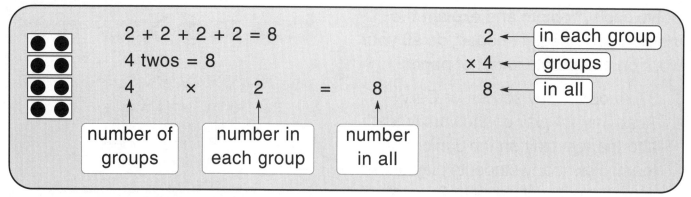

2 + 2 + 2 + 2 = 8

4 twos = 8

4　　×　　2　　=　　8

number of groups | number in each group | number in all

2 ← in each group
× 4 ← groups
8 ← in all

Write an addition sentence and a multiplication sentence to show how many in all.

1.

4 + 4 = 8

4 × 2 = 8

2.

3 + 3 + 3 = 9

3 × 3 = 9

3.

4 + 4 + 4 + 4 = 16

4 × 4 = 16

Solve each multiplication.

4. 1 × 5 _5_   **5.** 2 × 2 _4_   **6.** 2 × 4 _8_   **7.** 4 × 5 _20_   **8.** 3 × 5 _15_

9. 　6
　　×2
　　12

10. 　3
　　×4
　　12

11. 　5
　　×2
　　10

12. 　4
　　×2
　　8

13. 　3
　　×2
　　6

Problem Solving

14. Henry bought 3 bunches of bananas. There were 3 bananas to a bunch. How many bananas did he buy in all?

3 × 3 = 9; 9 bananas

15. Vivian bought 6 pairs of tennis shoes for her teammates. Each pair of shoes needed 2 shoelaces. How many shoelaces did Vivian buy altogether?

6 × 2 = 12; 12 shoelaces

One and Zero as Factors

Name _____

Date _____

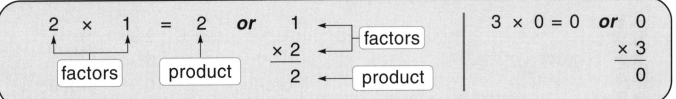

2 × 1 = 2 *or* 1 ← factors
factors product × 2 ←
2 ← product

3 × 0 = 0 *or* 0
× 3
0

Multiply.

1. 7 × 1 = __7__

2. 4 × 1 = __4__

3. 6 × 0 = __0__

4. 9 × 0 = __0__

5. 8 × 1 = __8__

6. 7 × 0 = __0__

7. 3 × 1 = __3__

8. 4 × 0 = __0__

9. 2 × 0 = __0__

Complete each multiplication

10. ☐ 0
  ×1
  0

11. 1
  ×☐ 1
  1

12. 1
  ×2
  2

13. ☐ 1
  ×3
  3

14. 1
  ×4
  4

15. 1
  ×☐ 5
  5

16. ☐ 0
  ×2
  0

17. ☐ 0
  ×3
  0

18. 0
  ×4
  0

19. 1
  ×5
  5

20. 1
  ×6
  6

21. ☐ 0
  ×7
  0

Problem Solving

22. My product is 5. One of my factors is 5. What is my other factor?

5 × 1 = 5; 1

23. One of my factors is 8. My product is 0. What is my other factor?

8 × 0 = 0; 0

24. Rosalie sent 1 postcard to each of her 7 friends. How many postcards did she send?

7 × 1 = 7; 7 postcards

Use with Lesson 4-2, text pages 134–135.

41

Multiply Twos

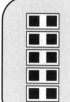 5 groups of 2   5 × 2 = 10   **or**   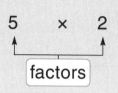 2 ← factors × 5 ← 10 ← product

Complete each multiplication.

1.

3 twos = __6__

3 × 2 = __6__

2.

2 twos = __4__

2 × 2 = __4__

3.

6 twos = __12__

6 × 2 = __12__

Multiply.

4.
$$\begin{array}{r} 2 \\ \times 4 \\ \hline 8 \end{array}$$

5.
$$\begin{array}{r} 2 \\ \times 8 \\ \hline 16 \end{array}$$

6.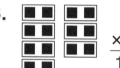
$$\begin{array}{r} 2 \\ \times 7 \\ \hline 14 \end{array}$$

Find the product.

7. 1 × 2 = __2__   **8.** 5 × 2 = __10__   **9.** 8 × 2 = __16__   **10.** 4 × 2 = __8__

11.
$$\begin{array}{r} 2 \\ \times 3 \\ \hline 6 \end{array}$$

12.
$$\begin{array}{r} 2 \\ \times 6 \\ \hline 12 \end{array}$$

13.
$$\begin{array}{r} 2 \\ \times 9 \\ \hline 18 \end{array}$$

14.
$$\begin{array}{r} 2 \\ \times 7 \\ \hline 14 \end{array}$$

15.
$$\begin{array}{r} 2 \\ \times 5 \\ \hline 10 \end{array}$$

16.
$$\begin{array}{r} 2 \\ \times 2 \\ \hline 4 \end{array}$$

Problem Solving

17. Ms. Johnson bought 9 packages of sponges. Each package contained 2 sponges. How many sponges did she buy?

9 × 2 = 18; 18 sponges

18. The factors are 7 and 2. What is the product?

7 × 2 = 14

Multiply Threes

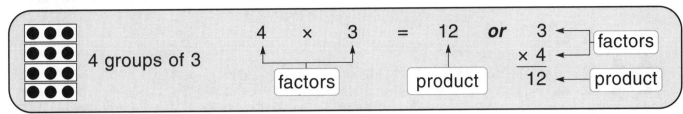

4 groups of 3

$4 \times 3 = 12$ **or** $\begin{array}{r} 3 \\ \times 4 \\ \hline 12 \end{array}$ — factors / product

factors   product

Complete each multiplication.

1.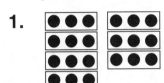

   7 threes = __21__

   $7 \times 3 = $ __21__

2. 5 threes = __15__

   $5 \times 3 = $ __15__

3. 6 threes = __18__

   $6 \times 3 = $ __18__

Multiply.

4. $\begin{array}{r} 3 \\ \times 2 \\ \hline 6 \end{array}$

5. $\begin{array}{r} 3 \\ \times 5 \\ \hline 15 \end{array}$

6. $\begin{array}{r} 3 \\ \times 4 \\ \hline 12 \end{array}$

Find the product.

7. $8 \times 3 = $ __24__

8. $2 \times 3 = $ __6__

9. $9 \times 3 = $ __27__

10. $4 \times 3 = $ __12__

11. $\begin{array}{r} 3 \\ \times 7 \\ \hline 21 \end{array}$

12. $\begin{array}{r} 3 \\ \times 9 \\ \hline 27 \end{array}$

13. $\begin{array}{r} 3 \\ \times 1 \\ \hline 3 \end{array}$

14. $\begin{array}{r} 3 \\ \times 8 \\ \hline 24 \end{array}$

15. $\begin{array}{r} 3 \\ \times 3 \\ \hline 9 \end{array}$

16. $\begin{array}{r} 3 \\ \times 6 \\ \hline 18 \end{array}$

Problem Solving

17. Jamal sold cards to raise money for the school band. Nine people each bought 3 boxes of cards. How many boxes did he sell?

    $9 \times 3 = 27$; 27 boxes

18. Chris won 2 sets of books for selling the most cards. Each set had 3 books. How many books did he win altogether?

    $2 \times 3 = 6$; 6 books

Use with Lesson 4-4, text pages 138–139.

43

Multiply Fours

 4 groups of 4   4 × 4 = 16   *or* $\begin{array}{r} 4 \\ \times\,4 \\ \hline 16 \end{array}$

Complete each multiplication.

1.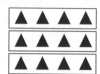

    6 fours = __24__

    6 × 4 = __24__

2.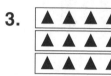

    3 fours = __12__

    3 × 4 = __12__

3.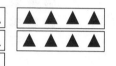

    5 fours = __20__

    5 × 4 = __20__

Find the product.

4. $\begin{array}{r} 4 \\ \times\,8 \\ \hline 32 \end{array}$
5. $\begin{array}{r} 4 \\ \times\,5 \\ \hline 20 \end{array}$
6. $\begin{array}{r} 4 \\ \times\,2 \\ \hline 8 \end{array}$
7. $\begin{array}{r} 4 \\ \times\,9 \\ \hline 36 \end{array}$
8. $\begin{array}{r} 4 \\ \times\,1 \\ \hline 4 \end{array}$
9. $\begin{array}{r} 4 \\ \times\,7 \\ \hline 28 \end{array}$

10. 9 × 4 = __36__   11. 3 × 4 = __12__   12. 7 × 4 = __28__   13. 8 × 4 = __32__

14. 6 × 4 = __24__   15. 1 × 4 = __4__   16. 4 × 4 = __16__   17. 5 × 4 = __20__

18. 8 × 4 = __32__   19. 0 × 4 = __0__   20. 9 × 4 = __36__   21. 2 × 4 = __8__

Problem Solving

22. Lori made 3 salads. Each salad had 4 tomatoes. How many tomatoes did she use?

       __3 × 4 = 12; 12 tomatoes__

23. Carlos made 8 sandwiches. Each sandwich had 4 slices of turkey. How many turkey slices did he use?

       __4 × 8 = 32; 32 turkey slices__

Multiply Fives

Name _____

Date _____

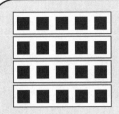 4 groups of 5   4 × 5 = 20   **or**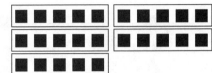

Complete each multiplication.

1.

2 fives = __10__

2 × 5 = __10__

2.

1 five = __5__

1 × 5 = __5__

3.

5 fives = __25__

5 × 5 = __25__

Write a multiplication sentence for each model.

4.

5 × 4 = 20

5.

5 × 6 = 30

Find the product.

6. 1 × 5 = __5__   **7.** 8 × 5 = __40__   **8.** 9 × 5 = __45__   **9.** 3 × 5 = __15__

10. 7 × 5 = __35__   **11.** 6 × 5 = __30__   **12.** 4 × 5 = __20__   **13.** 2 × 5 = __10__

14.   5
      × 2
      ___
       10

15.   5
      × 7
      ___
       35

16.   5
      × 5
      ___
       25

17.   5
      × 6
      ___
       30

18.   5
      × 3
      ___
       15

19.   5
      × 9
      ___
       45

Problem Solving

20. Michael made party bags for 4 friends.
He put 5 sticks of gum in each bag.
How many sticks of gum did he use?   4 × 5 = 20; 20 sticks

21. Michael received 2 sets of markers at his
birthday party. Each set had 5 markers.
How many markers did he receive altogether?   2 × 5 = 10; 10 markers

Multiply Cents

Name _____

Date _____

3¢ ← cents in each group
× 2 ← number of groups
6¢ ← cents in all

Multiply first. Write the ¢ sign when needed.

1.

2.

$$\begin{array}{r} 4¢ \\ \times 3 \\ \hline 12¢ \end{array}$$

$$\begin{array}{r} 3¢ \\ \times 3 \\ \hline 9¢ \end{array}$$

3. $\begin{array}{r} 2¢ \\ \times 8 \\ \hline 16¢ \end{array}$ **4.** $\begin{array}{r} 3¢ \\ \times 0 \\ \hline 0¢ \end{array}$ **5.** $\begin{array}{r} 5¢ \\ \times 5 \\ \hline 25¢ \end{array}$ **6.** $\begin{array}{r} 2¢ \\ \times 6 \\ \hline 12¢ \end{array}$ **7.** $\begin{array}{r} 1¢ \\ \times 8 \\ \hline 8¢ \end{array}$ **8.** $\begin{array}{r} 4¢ \\ \times 5 \\ \hline 20¢ \end{array}$

9. $\begin{array}{r} 2¢ \\ \times 7 \\ \hline 14¢ \end{array}$ **10.** $\begin{array}{r} 4¢ \\ \times 8 \\ \hline 32¢ \end{array}$ **11.** $\begin{array}{r} 1¢ \\ \times 2 \\ \hline 2¢ \end{array}$ **12.** $\begin{array}{r} 4¢ \\ \times 7 \\ \hline 28¢ \end{array}$ **13.** $\begin{array}{r} 4¢ \\ \times 10 \\ \hline 40¢ \end{array}$ **14.** $\begin{array}{r} 5¢ \\ \times 3 \\ \hline 15¢ \end{array}$

15. $\begin{array}{r} 5 \\ \times 7 \\ \hline 35 \end{array}$ **16.** $\begin{array}{r} 3¢ \\ \times 8 \\ \hline 24¢ \end{array}$ **17.** $\begin{array}{r} 0 \\ \times 9 \\ \hline 0 \end{array}$ **18.** $\begin{array}{r} 4¢ \\ \times 9 \\ \hline 36¢ \end{array}$ **19.** $\begin{array}{r} 5¢ \\ \times 7 \\ \hline 35¢ \end{array}$ **20.** $\begin{array}{r} 1 \\ \times 6 \\ \hline 6 \end{array}$

Multiply mentally.

21. 4 × 4¢ = __16¢__

22. 2 × 1 = __2__

23. 8 × 5 = __40__

24. 4 × 0 = __0__

25. 5 × 2¢ = __10¢__

26. 7 × 3 = __21__

Problem Solving

27. Pat bought 4 toy charms. Each charm cost 5¢. How much money did she spend? ___4 × 5¢ = 20¢; 20¢___

28. Charles bought 6 stickers. Each sticker cost 4¢. How much money did he spend? ___6 × 4¢ = 24¢; 24¢___

Sums, Differences, and Products

Name _____

Date _____

Add to find sums.	Subtract to find differences.	Multiply to find products.
$\begin{array}{r} \scriptstyle 1\ 1 \\ 1476 \\ +6059 \\ \hline 7535 \end{array}$ ← sum	$\begin{array}{r} \scriptstyle 8\ 10\ 6\ 15 \\ 9\cancel{0}7\cancel{5} \\ -1827 \\ \hline 7248 \end{array}$ ← difference	$\begin{array}{r} 3 \\ \times 5 \\ \hline 15 \end{array}$ ← product

Add, subtract, or multiply. Watch the signs.

1.
$\begin{array}{r} 428 \\ +\ 36 \\ \hline 464 \end{array}$

2.
$\begin{array}{r} 8094 \\ +1093 \\ \hline 9187 \end{array}$

3.
$\begin{array}{r} 3¢ \\ \times 9 \\ \hline 27¢ \end{array}$

4.
$\begin{array}{r} 1 \\ \times 9 \\ \hline 9 \end{array}$

5.
$\begin{array}{r} 6035 \\ -2508 \\ \hline 3527 \end{array}$

6.
$\begin{array}{r} 2 \\ \times 5 \\ \hline 10 \end{array}$

7.
$\begin{array}{r} 5 \\ \times 6 \\ \hline 30 \end{array}$

8.
$\begin{array}{r} \$8.26 \\ +\ 4.07 \\ \hline \$12.33 \end{array}$

9.
$\begin{array}{r} 3672 \\ -\ 489 \\ \hline 3183 \end{array}$

10.
$\begin{array}{r} 0 \\ \times 8 \\ \hline 0 \end{array}$

11.
$\begin{array}{r} 43 \\ +19 \\ \hline 62 \end{array}$

12.
$\begin{array}{r} 4¢ \\ \times 2 \\ \hline 8¢ \end{array}$

13.
$\begin{array}{r} \$4.82 \\ -\ 2.70 \\ \hline \$2.12 \end{array}$

14.
$\begin{array}{r} 596 \\ +324 \\ \hline 920 \end{array}$

15.
$\begin{array}{r} \$31.67 \\ +\ 42.85 \\ \hline \$74.52 \end{array}$

16.
$\begin{array}{r} \$.81 \\ -\ .65 \\ \hline \$.16 \end{array}$

Problem Solving

17. An adult has 206 bones. A newborn baby has 300 bones. How many more bones does a baby have than an adult? _300 − 206 = 94; 94 more bones_

18. The spine has 26 bones. The chest has 25 bones. How many bones are in the chest and spine altogether? _26 + 25 = 51; 51 bones_

19. There are 5 bones in each palm. How many bones are in two palms? _2 × 5 = 10; 10 bones_

 47

Order in Multiplication

Name _____

Date _____

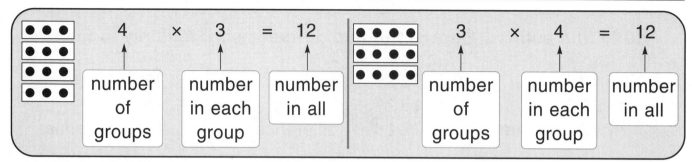

Find the product.

1. $8 \times 5 =$ __40__   2. $7 \times 4 =$ __28__   3. $9 \times 3 =$ __27__   4. $6 \times 3 =$ __18__

    $5 \times 8 =$ __40__ $4 \times 7 =$ __28__ $3 \times 9 =$ __27__ $3 \times 6 =$ __18__

5. $6 \times 2 =$ __12__   6. $5 \times 3 =$ __15__   7. $9 \times 0 =$ __0__   8. $7 \times 1 =$ __7__

    $2 \times 6 =$ __12__ $3 \times 5 =$ __15__ $0 \times 9 =$ __0__ $1 \times 7 =$ __7__

Multiply.

9. $\begin{array}{r} 4 \\ \times 5 \\ \hline 20 \end{array}$ $\begin{array}{r} 5 \\ \times 4 \\ \hline 20 \end{array}$ 10. $\begin{array}{r} 3 \\ \times 7 \\ \hline 21 \end{array}$ $\begin{array}{r} 7 \\ \times 3 \\ \hline 21 \end{array}$ 11. $\begin{array}{r} 5 \\ \times 2 \\ \hline 10 \end{array}$ $\begin{array}{r} 2 \\ \times 5 \\ \hline 10 \end{array}$

12. $\begin{array}{r} 7 \\ \times 5 \\ \hline 35 \end{array}$ $\begin{array}{r} 5 \\ \times 7 \\ \hline 35 \end{array}$ 13. $\begin{array}{r} 6 \\ \times 4 \\ \hline 24 \end{array}$ $\begin{array}{r} 4 \\ \times 6 \\ \hline 24 \end{array}$ 14. $\begin{array}{r} 9 \\ \times 4 \\ \hline 36 \end{array}$ $\begin{array}{r} 4 \\ \times 9 \\ \hline 36 \end{array}$

Find the missing factor.

15. $4 \times 8 =$ __8__ $\times 4$ 16. $9 \times 2 = 2 \times$ __9__   17. __1__ $\times 6 =$ __6__ $\times 1$

18. $3 \times$ __8__ $= 8 \times$ __3__   19. $7 \times 2 =$ __2__ $\times$ __7__   20. $6 \times 5 =$ __5__ $\times$ __6__

Problem Solving

21. Anne put 2 labels on each of her video cassettes. She owns 9 video cassettes. How many labels did she use?

    _____ $9 \times 2 = 18$; 18 labels _____

22. Manuel made 2 cakes for his brother's birthday party. He used 3 eggs in each. How many eggs did he use in all?

    _____ $2 \times 3 = 6$; 6 eggs _____

Missing Factors

Name _____

Date _____

$$\underset{\text{factors}}{\underline{?} \quad \times \quad \underline{3}} \quad = \quad \underset{\text{product}}{12} \quad \longrightarrow \quad 4 \quad \times \quad 3 \quad = \quad 12$$

4 is the missing factor.

Find the missing factor.

1.
$$\begin{array}{r} 2 \\ \times \boxed{6} \\ \hline 12 \end{array}$$

2.
$$\begin{array}{r} \boxed{5} \\ \times 3 \\ \hline 15 \end{array}$$

3.
$$\begin{array}{r} \boxed{4} \\ \times 8 \\ \hline 32 \end{array}$$

4.
$$\begin{array}{r} 8 \\ \times \boxed{2} \\ \hline 16 \end{array}$$

5.
$$\begin{array}{r} 5 \\ \times \boxed{4} \\ \hline 20 \end{array}$$

6.
$$\begin{array}{r} \boxed{4} \\ \times 3 \\ \hline 12 \end{array}$$

7.
$$\begin{array}{r} \boxed{4} \\ \times 6 \\ \hline 24 \end{array}$$

8.
$$\begin{array}{r} 7 \\ \times \boxed{5} \\ \hline 35 \end{array}$$

9.
$$\begin{array}{r} 7 \\ \times \boxed{2} \\ \hline 14 \end{array}$$

10.
$$\begin{array}{r} \boxed{3} \\ \times 3 \\ \hline 9 \end{array}$$

11.
$$\begin{array}{r} \boxed{3} \\ \times 2 \\ \hline 6 \end{array}$$

12.
$$\begin{array}{r} 7 \\ \times \boxed{3} \\ \hline 21 \end{array}$$

13. $2 \times \underline{4} = 8$

14. $\underline{8} \times 5 = 40$

15. $7 \times \underline{2} = 14$

16. $\underline{4} \times 5 = 20$

17. $\underline{9} \times 5 = 45$

18. $4 \times \underline{4} = 16$

19. $18 = 3 \times \underline{6}$

20. $9 = 9 \times \underline{1}$

21. $28 = 7 \times \underline{4}$

Complete the table.

22.

factor	factor	product
8	3	24
3	6	18
5	4	20

23.

factor	factor	product
9	3	27
9	5	45
8	4	32

Problem Solving

24. Wendy put 16 carrots in bunches. She put 4 carrots in each bunch. How many bunches did she have? $\underline{16 = 4 \times 4; \ 4 \text{ bunches}}$

25. Dave sewed 14 sails. He put the sails on 7 boats. Each boat had the same number of sails. How many did he put on each boat? $\underline{7 \times 2 = 14; \ 2 \text{ sails}}$

Problem-Solving Strategy: Use More Than One Step

Name _____

Date _____

There were 77 third graders in three rooms. There were 27 third graders in Room 101 and 25 in Room 102. How many third graders were in Room 103?

First find the number of third graders in Rooms 101 and 103.

Add: 27 + 25 = 52

Then find out how many are not in those rooms.

Subtract: 77 − 52 = 25

There were 25 third graders in Room 103.

Solve. Do your work on a separate sheet of paper.

1. Of 77 third graders, on Monday 3 were absent from Room 101, 4 were absent from Room 102, and 2 were absent from Room 103. How many third graders attended school that day?

   3 + 4 + 2 = 9; 77 − 9 = 68;
   68 third graders

2. Ms. Diaz gave 5 toothpicks to each of 9 children for an art project. The full box she started with held 100 toothpicks. How many toothpicks did she have left?

   9 × 5 = 45; 100 − 45 = 55;
   55 toothpicks

3. Ms. Diaz bought glue for $1.49 and poster paper for $4.50. How much change did she receive if she paid with a ten-dollar bill?

   $1.49 + $4.50 = $5.99;
   $10.00 − $5.99 = $4.01; $4.01

4. Mr. Vincent had a package of 35 pencils. He gave 2 pencils to each of 9 children. How many pencils did he have left?

   9 × 2 = 18; 35 − 18 = 17;
   17 pencils

5. At lunch, Alison spent $.25 for milk and $.35 for an orange. She gave the cashier $1.00. What was her change?

   $.25 + $.35 = $.60;
   $1.00 − $.60 = $.40; $.40

6. Mr. Wilbur gave 2 animal books to each of 5 children and 3 puzzle books to each of 4 children. How many books did he give to the children in all?

   5 × 2 = 10; 4 × 3 = 12;
   10 + 12 = 22; 22 books

Problem-Solving Applications: Mixed Review

Name _____

Date _____

Solve each problem and explain the method you used. If needed, do all your work on a separate sheet of paper.

Read > Plan > Solve > Check

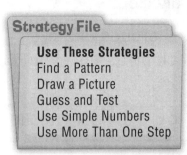

Strategy File

Use These Strategies
Find a Pattern
Draw a Picture
Guess and Test
Use Simple Numbers
Use More Than One Step

1. Philip has 4 packs of baseball cards. Each pack contains 8 cards. How many cards does Philip have in all?

$8 \times 4 = 32$; 32 cards

2. Mai's red shoes cost $27.00. Her blue shoes cost $4.00 more than the red shoes. Her green shoes cost $6.00 less than her blue shoes. How much are Mai's green shoes?

$27.00 + $4.00 = $31.00; $31.00 − $6.00 = $25.00; green shoes cost $25.00

3. A fruit stand started with 40 oranges. It sold 2 on Tuesday, 4 on Wednesday, 6 on Thursday, and so on. How many oranges will be left at the end of the day Saturday?

$2 + 4 + 6 + 8 + 10 = 30$; $40 − 30 = 10$; 10 oranges left

4. Louise buys eight 6-packs of soda. She drinks two of the sodas. How many sodas does Louise have left?

$8 \times 6 = 48$; $48 − 2 = 46$; 46 sodas

5. Ralph washes his neighbor's car. The neighbor pays him $6.75 and gives him a 3 quarter tip. How much was Ralph paid in all?

3 quarters = 75¢; $6.75 + $0.75 = $7.50; $7.50

6. There are 18 bikes in a bike rack. There are 4 more blue bikes than yellow bikes, and 2 less yellow bikes than green bikes. How many bikes of each color are in the rack?

8 blue bikes; 4 yellow bikes; 6 green bikes

7. Maria, George, and Diane all ran for class president. Maria received 38 votes. George received 71 votes. Diane received 63 votes. How many total people voted in the election?

$38 + 71 + 63 = 172$; 172 people voted

8. Thelma has 36 CDs in her carrying case. It can hold 54 CDs. How many more CDs can Thelma put in the case?

$54 − 36 = 18$; 18 more CDs

9. Harvey, Rita, and Katrina each worked 6 hours at the grocery store. How many hours did they work altogether?

$6 \times 3 = 18$; 18 hours altogether

 51

Understand Division

Name _____

Date _____

You can use repeated subtraction to solve division.

How many groups of 2 are in 10? Count back by 2s until you reach 0.

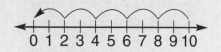

Or you can write a division sentence to show how many groups of 2 are in 10.

10 ÷ 2 = 5

| number in all | number in each group | number of groups |

Find how many groups.
Use repeated subtraction or write a division sentence.

1. 12 in all
6 in each group

_____2 groups_____

2. 16 in all
4 in each group

_____4 groups_____

3. 8 in all
2 in each group

_____4 groups_____

4. 15 in all
5 in each group

_____3 groups_____

5. 18 in all
6 in each group

_____3 groups_____

6. 30 in all
5 in each group

_____6 groups_____

Find how many in each group.
Use repeated subtraction or write a division sentence.

7. 8 in all
2 groups

_____4 in each group_____

8. 10 in all
5 groups

_____2 in each group_____

9. 12 in all
3 groups

_____4 in each group_____

10. 18 in all
9 groups

_____2 in each group_____

11. 6 in all
3 groups

_____2 in each group_____

12. 25 in all
5 groups

_____5 in each group_____

13. 30 in all
6 groups

_____5 in each group_____

14. 10 in all
5 groups

_____2 in each group_____

15. 24 in all
6 groups

_____4 in each group_____

One and Zero in Division

> The **dividend** is the number you divide.
> The **divisor** is the number you divide by.
> The **quotient** is the answer.

dividend	divisor	quotient	
0	÷ 2	= 0	or $2\overline{)0}$

quotient ← 0
dividend ← $2\overline{)0}$
divisor ↑

Write the quotient. You may use counters.

1. $6 \div 1 = \underline{6}$ **2.** $0 \div 5 = \underline{0}$ **3.** $2 \div 2 = \underline{1}$

4. $0 \div 3 = \underline{0}$ **5.** $4 \div 4 = \underline{1}$ **6.** $7 \div 1 = \underline{7}$

7. $1 \div 1 = \underline{1}$ **8.** $8 \div 8 = \underline{1}$ **9.** $0 \div 9 = \underline{0}$

10. $7 \div 7 = \underline{1}$ **11.** $0 \div 6 = \underline{0}$ **12.** $5 \div 1 = \underline{5}$

13. $3 \div 1 = \underline{3}$ **14.** $8 \div 1 = \underline{8}$ **15.** $0 \div 2 = \underline{0}$

16. $0 \div 4 = \underline{0}$ **17.** $9 \div 9 = \underline{1}$ **18.** $6 \div 6 = \underline{1}$

19. $7\overline{)0}^{\,0}$ **20.** $5\overline{)5}^{\,1}$ **21.** $1\overline{)2}^{\,2}$ **22.** $8\overline{)8}^{\,1}$ **23.** $1\overline{)9}^{\,9}$ **24.** $8\overline{)0}^{\,0}$

Problem Solving

25. Five friends shared 5 apples equally. How many apples did each friend get?

$5 \div 5 = 1$; 1 apple

26. There are 4 pears in all. How many pears are in 1 group?

$4 \div 1 = 4$; 4 pears

27. The dividend is 0. The divisor is 5. What is the quotient?

$0 \div 5 = 0$; 0

53

Divide by 2

Name _____

Date _____

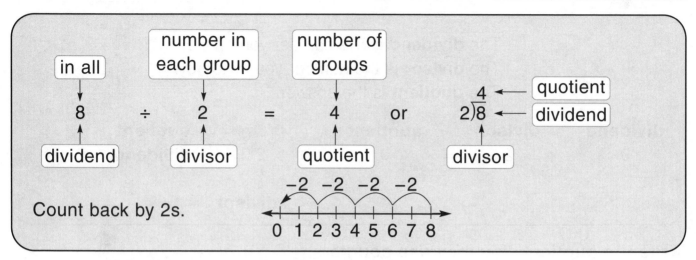

Write a division sentence for each model.

1.

   $4 \div 2 = 2$

2.

   $12 \div 2 = 6$

3.

   $6 \div 2 = 3$

Find the quotient.

4. $2 \div 2 = \underline{1}$

5. $10 \div 2 = \underline{5}$

6. $14 \div 2 = \underline{7}$

7. $18 \div 2 = \underline{9}$

8. $8 \div 2 = \underline{4}$

9. $16 \div 2 = \underline{8}$

10. $0 \div 2 = \underline{0}$

11. $4 \div 2 = \underline{2}$

12. $12 \div 2 = \underline{6}$

13. $2\overline{)6}$ → 3

14. $2\overline{)18}$ → 9

15. $2\overline{)10}$ → 5

16. $2\overline{)8}$ → 4

17. $2\overline{)4}$ → 2

18. $2\overline{)16}$ → 8

19. $2\overline{)2}$ → 1

20. $2\overline{)14}$ → 7

21. $2\overline{)0}$ → 0

22. $2\overline{)12}$ → 6

Problem Solving

23. Shauna sold 16 boxes of cookies.
    She sold 2 boxes to each customer.
    How many customers did she have?

    $16 \div 2 = 8$; 8 customers

24. Jason has 18 white socks. How many
    pairs of white socks does he have?

    $18 \div 2 = 9$; 9 pairs

---

54   **Use with Lesson 5-3, text pages 166–167.**

Divide by 3

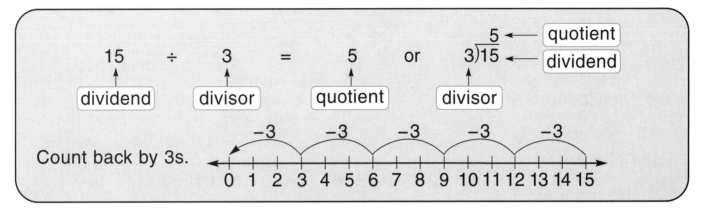

Write a division sentence for each model.

1. [★★★ / ★★★]

$\underline{\quad 6 \div 3 = 2 \quad}$

2. [★★★ / ★★★ / ★★★ / ★★★]

$\underline{\quad 12 \div 3 = 4 \quad}$

3. [★★★ ★★★ / ★★★ ★★★ / ★★★ / ★★★]

$\underline{\quad 18 \div 3 = 6 \quad}$

Find the quotient.

4. $3\overline{)27}$ → 9

5. $3\overline{)9}$ → 3

6. $3\overline{)15}$ → 5

7. $3\overline{)24}$ → 8

8. $3\overline{)6}$ → 2

9. $3\overline{)3}$ → 1

10. $3\overline{)12}$ → 4

11. $3\overline{)21}$ → 7

12. $3\overline{)18}$ → 6

13. $3\overline{)0}$ → 0

14. $24 \div 3 =$ __8__

15. $27 \div 3 =$ __9__

16. $0 \div 3 =$ __0__

17. $15 \div 3 =$ __5__

18. $21 \div 3 =$ __7__

19. $6 \div 3 =$ __2__

20. $3 \div 3 =$ __1__

21. $18 \div 3 =$ __6__

22. $9 \div 3 =$ __3__

Problem Solving

23. Jason has 6 toy airplanes. He puts them in 3 equal groups. How many toy airplanes are in each group?

$\underline{\quad 6 \div 3 = 2; \text{ 2 in each group} \quad}$

24. Wanda has 12 stuffed bears. She puts 3 bears on each shelf. How many shelves does she use?

$\underline{\quad 12 \div 3 = 4; \text{ 4 shelves} \quad}$

 55

Divide by 4

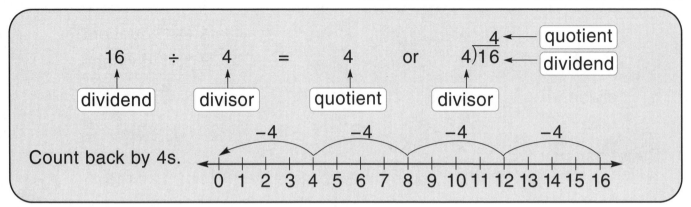

Write a division sentence for each model.

1. ☆☆☆☆ / ☆☆☆☆ / ☆☆☆☆

___12 ÷ 4 = 3___

2. ☆☆☆☆

___4 ÷ 4 = 1___

3. ☆☆☆☆ / ☆☆☆☆

___8 ÷ 4 = 2___

Find the quotient.

4. 36 ÷ 4 = ___9___

5. 16 ÷ 4 = ___4___

6. 28 ÷ 4 = ___7___

7. 20 ÷ 4 = ___5___

8. 32 ÷ 4 = ___8___

9. 24 ÷ 4 = ___6___

10. $4\overline{)20}$ = 5

11. $4\overline{)28}$ = 7

12. $4\overline{)16}$ = 4

13. $4\overline{)32}$ = 8

14. $4\overline{)24}$ = 6

15. $4\overline{)4}$ = 1

16. $4\overline{)12}$ = 3

17. $4\overline{)0}$ = 0

18. $4\overline{)8}$ = 2

19. $4\overline{)36}$ = 9

Problem Solving

20. Sonia has a rock collection. She took 24 rocks and put 4 rocks in each box. How many boxes did she use?

___24 ÷ 4 = 6; 6 boxes___

21. Peter made 4 boxes to hold all of his 16 model cars. He put the same number of cars into each box. How many were in each box?

___16 ÷ 4 = 4; 4 cars___

56   **Use with Lesson 5-5, text pages 170–171.**

Divide by 5

Name _____

Date _____

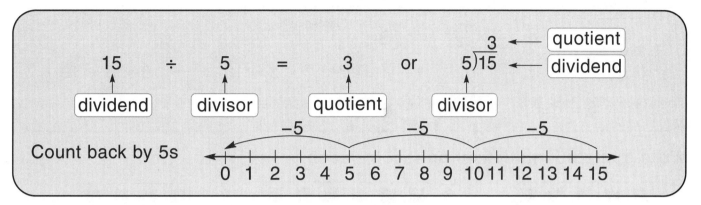

Write a division sentence for each model.

1. ☆☆☆☆☆ ☆☆☆☆☆
☆☆☆☆☆ ☆☆☆☆☆
☆☆☆☆☆ ☆☆☆☆☆

$30 \div 5 = 6$

2. ■ ■ ■ ■ ■

$5 \div 5 = 1$

3. ●●●●●
●●●●●
●●●●●

$15 \div 5 = 3$

Divide.

4. $25 \div 5 = \underline{5}$

5. $10 \div 5 = \underline{2}$

6. $40 \div 5 = \underline{8}$

7. $45 \div 5 = \underline{9}$

8. $20 \div 5 = \underline{4}$

9. $35 \div 5 = \underline{7}$

10. $30 \div 5 = \underline{6}$

11. $5 \div 5 = \underline{1}$

12. $15 \div 5 = \underline{3}$

13. $5\overline{)40}$ 8

14. $5\overline{)30}$ 6

15. $5\overline{)5}$ 1

16. $5\overline{)15}$ 3

17. $5\overline{)45}$ 9

18. $5\overline{)25}$ 5

19. $5\overline{)0}$ 0

20. $5\overline{)20}$ 4

21. $5\overline{)35}$ 7

22. $5\overline{)10}$ 2

Problem Solving

23. Bernard gave 25 sheets of paper to 5 children. He gave the same number of sheets to each child. How many sheets of paper did each child receive?

$25 \div 5 = 5$; 5 sheets

24. Louise had 40 crayons. She put 5 crayons into each bag. How many bags did she use?

$40 \div 5 = 8$; 8 bags

Use with Lesson 5-6, text pages 172–173.

Relate Multiplication and Division

Name _____

Date _____

$18 \div 3 = \underline{?}$ or $3\overline{)18}^{?}$

So $18 \div 3 = 6$, or $3\overline{)18}^{6}$

Think: $\underline{?} \times 3 = 18 \longrightarrow 6 \times 3 = 18$

Write a related multiplication fact for each.

1.

$15 \div 5 = 3$
$\underline{3 \times 5 = 15}$

2.

$12 \div 3 = 4$
$\underline{4 \times 3 = 12}$

3.

$8 \div 4 = 2$
$\underline{2 \times 4 = 8}$

Write a multiplication sentence and a division sentence for each.

4.

$\underline{2 \times 5 = 10}$

$\underline{10 \div 5 = 2}$

5.

$\underline{3 \times 4 = 12}$

$\underline{12 \div 4 = 3}$

6.

$\underline{4 \times 4 = 16}$

$\underline{16 \div 4 = 4}$

Complete each multiplication and division sentence.

7. $3 \times 2 = \underline{6}$

$6 \div 2 = \underline{3}$

8. $6 \times 2 = \underline{12}$

$12 \div 2 = \underline{6}$

9. $9 \times 3 = \underline{27}$

$27 \div 3 = \underline{9}$

10. $4 \times 6 = \underline{24}$

$24 \div 6 = \underline{4}$

11. $4 \times 5 = \underline{20}$

$20 \div 5 = \underline{4}$

12. $8 \times 5 = \underline{40}$

$40 \div 5 = \underline{8}$

13. $7 \times 3 = \underline{21}$

$21 \div 3 = \underline{7}$

14. $6 \times 5 = \underline{30}$

$30 \div 5 = \underline{6}$

15. $\begin{array}{r} 2 \\ \times 7 \\ \hline 14 \end{array}$ $2\overline{)14}^{7}$

16. $\begin{array}{r} 3 \\ \times 8 \\ \hline 24 \end{array}$ $3\overline{)24}^{8}$

17. $\begin{array}{r} 2 \\ \times 9 \\ \hline 18 \end{array}$ $2\overline{)18}^{9}$

18. $\begin{array}{r} 5 \\ \times 7 \\ \hline 35 \end{array}$ $5\overline{)35}^{7}$

Problem Solving

19. Oranges come 4 to a pack. There are 28 oranges in all. How many packs are there? $\underline{28 \div 4 = 7;\ 7\ packs}$

Divide Cents

Name _____

Date _____

$12¢ \div 3 = 4¢$ or $3\overline{)12¢}^{4¢}$

↑ cents in all

↑ number of groups

↑ cents in each group

Divide. Remember to write the cent sign.

1. $4¢ \div 2 = \underline{2¢}$

2. $8¢ \div 1 = \underline{8¢}$

3. $18¢ \div 3 = \underline{6¢}$

4. $10¢ \div 2 = \underline{5¢}$

5. $32¢ \div 4 = \underline{8¢}$

6. $15¢ \div 5 = \underline{3¢}$

7. $5\overline{)35¢}^{7¢}$

8. $3\overline{)9¢}^{3¢}$

9. $1\overline{)3¢}^{3¢}$

10. $4\overline{)24¢}^{6¢}$

11. $2\overline{)14¢}^{7¢}$

12. $3\overline{)24¢}^{8¢}$

13. $5\overline{)10¢}^{2¢}$

14. $4\overline{)16¢}^{4¢}$

Multiply or divide.

15. $7 \times 4¢ = \underline{28¢}$

16. $9 \times 2¢ = \underline{18¢}$

17. $9 \times 5¢ = \underline{45¢}$

18. $9 \times 1 = \underline{9}$

19. $4 \times 5¢ = \underline{20¢}$

20. $9 \times 3¢ = \underline{27¢}$

21. $21¢ \div 3 = \underline{7¢}$

22. $18 \div 2 = \underline{9}$

23. $30¢ \div 5 = \underline{6¢}$

Problem Solving

24. Donna paid 40¢ for 5 stickers. She paid the same amount for each sticker. How much did each sticker cost?

$40¢ \div 5 = 8¢$; 8¢ per sticker

25. Emilio spent 36¢ for 4 pencils. Each pencil cost the same amount. How much did each pencil cost?

$36¢ \div 4 = 9¢$; 9¢ per pencil

 59

Function Machines

Name _____

Date _____

Rule × 3	
Input	**Output**
1 × 3	3
2 × 3	6
3 × 3	9
4 × 3	12

Rule ÷ 4	
Input	**Output**
16 ÷ 4	4
12 ÷ 4	3
8 ÷ 4	2
4 ÷ 4	1

Follow the rule to find the output.

1.

Rule × 2	
Input	**Output**
1	2
2	4
3	6
4	8
5	10
6	12
7	14
8	16

2.

Rule ÷ 6	
Input	**Output**
48	8
42	7
36	6
30	5
24	4
18	3
12	2
6	1

Problem Solving

Write the rule. Then solve the problem.

3. Jorge plays baseball when he gets home from school. He plays for 2 hours each day. How many hours does Jorge play baseball in 5 days?

Rule × 2; 5 × 2 = 10; 10 hours

4. Matt eats 3 eggs for breakfast every morning. How many eggs does he eat in a week?

Rule × 3; 1 week = 7 days; 7 × 3 = 21; 21 eggs

Problem-Solving Strategy: Write a Number Sentence

Name _____

Date _____

Add	• Join like sets or quantities.	
Subtract	• Separate, or take away from a set. • Compare two sets, or quantities.	• Find part of a set. • Find how many more are needed.
Multiply	• Join equal sets, or quantities.	
Divide	• Separate a set into equal groups.	• Share a set equally.

Write a number sentence to solve.

1. Germaine learned that humans will normally have 20 "baby" teeth and 32 permanent teeth. How many more permanent teeth than "baby" teeth do humans have?

   $32 - 20 = 12;$
   12 more permanent teeth

2. For the fair 22 students used plants in their experiments and 19 students used electricity. How many more students used plants than electricity?

   $22 - 19 = 3;$ 3 more students

3. On Monday morning, 28 students came to the fair. Then 37 came in the afternoon. How many students came to the fair in all?

   $28 + 37 = 65;$ 65 students

4. Anna placed 16 magnets on metal strips. She put groups of 4 magnets on each strip. How many strips did she use?

   $16 \div 4 = 4;$ 4 strips

5. There were 15 children who visited a special exhibit. They visited the exhibit in groups of 3. How many groups were there?

   $15 \div 3 = 5;$ 5 groups

6. The 5 tables at the Bay School science fair each held 4 experiments. How many experiments were there at the fair?

   $5 \times 4 = 20;$ 20 experiments

7. Carl used 15 glass items and 17 metal items in his recycling experiment. How many items did he use in all?

   $15 + 17 = 32;$ 32 items

8. Juan planted 8 seeds in each of 2 pots for his experiment. How many seeds did he plant?

   $2 \times 8 = 16;$ 16 seeds

Problem-Solving Applications: Mixed Review

Name _____

Date _____

Solve each problem and explain the method you used. If needed, do all your work on a separate sheet of paper.

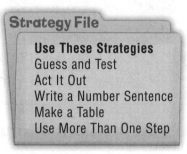

Strategy File

Use These Strategies
Guess and Test
Act It Out
Write a Number Sentence
Make a Table
Use More Than One Step

1. On Halloween, Mrs. Sadler gave 40 pieces of candy to 8 children. If she gave each child the same amount of candy, how many pieces did she give each child?

   $40 \div 8 = 5$; 5 pieces

2. There are 28 students in Mr. Williams' class. He divides the class into 4 equal groups. How many students are in each group?

   $28 \div 4 = 7$; 7 students

3. Carlos hiked three trails. Each trail took the same amount of time to complete. If he hiked for a total of 12 hours, how much time did it take Carlos to complete each trail?

   $12 \div 3 = 4$; 4 hours

4. There are 22 players in a soccer game. The two teams have the same number of players. How many are on each team?

   $22 \div 2 = 11$; 11 players

5. Ian bought a 20-ride subway pass. He uses 2 rides a day to get to and from school. How many rides will he have left after 4 days?

   $4 \times 2 = 8$; $20 - 8 = 12$; 12 rides

6. Kendra pays $30 to fill her car with gas. Gas is $3 per gallon. How many gallons did she buy?

   $30 \div 3 = 10$; 10 gallons

7. Two numbers have a sum of 11. They have a product of 24. What are the numbers?

   $8 \times 3 = 24$; $8 + 3 = 11$; 8 and 3

8. Tino scored 24 points in a game. If all his points were from three-point baskets, how many baskets did he make? If they were from two-point baskets, how many baskets did Tino make?

   $24 \div 3 = 8$; 8 baskets
   $24 \div 2 = 12$; 12 baskets

9. In the grocery store, 4 people are waiting in each of the first six checkout lanes, while 3 people are waiting in each of the other four lanes. How many people are waiting in all?

   $6 \times 4 = 24$; $4 \times 3 = 12$;
   $24 + 12 = 36$; 36 people

Factors and Products

Name _____

Date _____

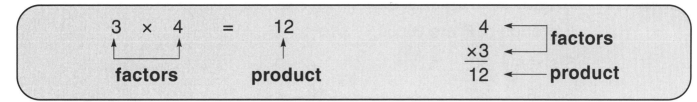

$$3 \times 4 = 12$$

factors   product

$$\begin{array}{r} 4 \\ \times 3 \\ \hline 12 \end{array}$$ factors

product

Complete each table.

1.

$\square \times 3$

IN	0	2	5	1	7	3	9
OUT	0	6	15	3	21	9	27

2.

$\square \times 5$

IN	4	9	1	2	6	0	3
OUT	20	45	5	10	30	0	15

3.

$\square \times 2$

IN	8	5	3	0	7	4	2
OUT	16	10	6	0	14	8	4

Write the product.

4. $\begin{array}{r} 5 \\ \times 3 \\ \hline 15 \end{array}$ **5.** $\begin{array}{r} 4 \\ \times 2 \\ \hline 8 \end{array}$ **6.** $\begin{array}{r} 4 \\ \times 5 \\ \hline 20 \end{array}$ **7.** $\begin{array}{r} 3 \\ \times 2 \\ \hline 6 \end{array}$ **8.** $\begin{array}{r} 5 \\ \times 2 \\ \hline 10 \end{array}$ **9.** $\begin{array}{r} 4 \\ \times 3 \\ \hline 12 \end{array}$

10. $\begin{array}{r} 4 \\ \times 6 \\ \hline 24 \end{array}$ **11.** $\begin{array}{r} 4 \\ \times 4 \\ \hline 16 \end{array}$ **12.** $\begin{array}{r} 5 \\ \times 4 \\ \hline 20 \end{array}$ **13.** $\begin{array}{r} 2 \\ \times 7 \\ \hline 14 \end{array}$ **14.** $\begin{array}{r} 2 \\ \times 2 \\ \hline 4 \end{array}$ **15.** $\begin{array}{r} 3 \\ \times 3 \\ \hline 9 \end{array}$

16. $\begin{array}{r} 0 \\ \times 3 \\ \hline 0 \end{array}$ **17.** $\begin{array}{r} 2 \\ \times 9 \\ \hline 18 \end{array}$ **18.** $\begin{array}{r} 4 \\ \times 7 \\ \hline 28 \end{array}$ **19.** $\begin{array}{r} 2 \\ \times 3 \\ \hline 6 \end{array}$ **20.** $\begin{array}{r} 4 \\ \times 8 \\ \hline 32 \end{array}$ **21.** $\begin{array}{r} 5 \\ \times 6 \\ \hline 30 \end{array}$

Problem Solving

22. Jennifer collects 4 rocks on each of 7 days. How many rocks does Jennifer collect in all?

$7 \times 4 = 28$; 28 rocks

Use with Lesson 6-1, text page 190.

Multiply Sixes

Name _____

Date _____

5 groups of 6 are 30.

5 sixes = 30

5 × 6 = 30

groups ↑ in each group ↑ in all ↑

$$\begin{array}{r} 6 \\ \times 5 \\ \hline 30 \end{array}$$

★ ★ ★ ★ ★ ★
★ ★ ★ ★ ★ ★
★ ★ ★ ★ ★ ★
★ ★ ★ ★ ★ ★
★ ★ ★ ★ ★ ★

Write the product.

1. 7 × 6 = __42__   **2.** 10 × 6 = __60__   **3.** 2 × 6 = __12__   **4.** 9 × 6¢ = __54¢__

5. 4 × 6 = __24__   **6.** 3¢ × 6 = __18¢__   **7.** 8 × 6 = __48__   **8.** 6 × 6 = __36__

Multiply.

9. $\begin{array}{r} 6 \\ \times 3 \\ \hline 18 \end{array}$ **10.** $\begin{array}{r} 6 \\ \times 7¢ \\ \hline 42¢ \end{array}$ **11.** $\begin{array}{r} 6 \\ \times 8 \\ \hline 48 \end{array}$ **12.** $\begin{array}{r} 6 \\ \times 2 \\ \hline 12 \end{array}$ **13.** $\begin{array}{r} 6 \\ \times 1 \\ \hline 6 \end{array}$ **14.** $\begin{array}{r} 6 \\ \times 5 \\ \hline 30 \end{array}$

15. $\begin{array}{r} 6 \\ \times 4 \\ \hline 24 \end{array}$ **16.** $\begin{array}{r} 5 \\ \times 6 \\ \hline 30 \end{array}$ **17.** $\begin{array}{r} 2¢ \\ \times 6 \\ \hline 12¢ \end{array}$ **18.** $\begin{array}{r} 4 \\ \times 6 \\ \hline 24 \end{array}$ **19.** $\begin{array}{r} 6¢ \\ \times 6 \\ \hline 36¢ \end{array}$ **20.** $\begin{array}{r} 6 \\ \times 9 \\ \hline 54 \end{array}$

21. $\begin{array}{r} 1 \\ \times 6 \\ \hline 6 \end{array}$ **22.** $\begin{array}{r} 6 \\ \times 0 \\ \hline 0 \end{array}$ **23.** $\begin{array}{r} 6 \\ \times 7 \\ \hline 42 \end{array}$ **24.** $\begin{array}{r} 6¢ \\ \times 6 \\ \hline 36¢ \end{array}$ **25.** $\begin{array}{r} 0 \\ \times 6 \\ \hline 0 \end{array}$ **26.** $\begin{array}{r} 3 \\ \times 6 \\ \hline 18 \end{array}$

Problem Solving

27. There are 6 party horns in a pack. How many are there in 3 packs?

__3 × 6 = 18; 18 party horns__

28. Maria bought a package of stickers. There were 9 pages with 6 stickers on each page. How many stickers did she buy?

__9 × 6 = 54; 54 stickers__

29. There are 6 fish in each of 5 tanks in the pet store. How many fish are there in all?

__5 × 6 = 30; 30 fish__

Multiply Sevens

Name _____

Date _____

7 groups of 7 are 49.

7 sevens = 49

7 × 7   = 49

$$\begin{array}{r} 7 \\ \times 7 \\ \hline 49 \end{array}$$

Complete each multiplication fact.

1. ___4___ × 7 = ___28___

2. ___8___ × 7 = ___56___

3. ___6___ × 7 = ___42___

Write the product.

4. 7 × 7 = ___49___   **5.** 1 × 7 = ___7___   **6.** 2 × 7¢ = ___14¢___   **7.** 5 × 7 = ___35___

8. 0 × 7 = ___0___   **9.** 8 × 7¢ = ___56¢___   **10.** 3 × 7 = ___21___   **11.** 6 × 7 = ___42___

12. 9 × 7¢ = ___63¢___   **13.** 7 × 4 = ___28___   **14.** 7 × 2¢ = ___14¢___   **15.** 4 × 7 = ___28___

Multiply.

16. $\begin{array}{r} 7 \\ \times 3 \\ \hline 21 \end{array}$ **17.** $\begin{array}{r} 7 \\ \times 7 \\ \hline 49 \end{array}$ **18.** $\begin{array}{r} 7 \\ \times 8¢ \\ \hline 56¢ \end{array}$ **19.** $\begin{array}{r} 7 \\ \times 2 \\ \hline 14 \end{array}$ **20.** $\begin{array}{r} 7 \\ \times 10 \\ \hline 70 \end{array}$ **21.** $\begin{array}{r} 7 \\ \times 5¢ \\ \hline 35¢ \end{array}$

22. $\begin{array}{r} 7 \\ \times 4¢ \\ \hline 28¢ \end{array}$ **23.** $\begin{array}{r} 7 \\ \times 0 \\ \hline 0 \end{array}$ **24.** $\begin{array}{r} 2 \\ \times 7 \\ \hline 14 \end{array}$ **25.** $\begin{array}{r} 7 \\ \times 9¢ \\ \hline 63¢ \end{array}$ **26.** $\begin{array}{r} 7 \\ \times 6 \\ \hline 42 \end{array}$ **27.** $\begin{array}{r} 3 \\ \times 7 \\ \hline 21 \end{array}$

Problem Solving

28. Gina's swim team took part in 4 events. They won 7 ribbons in each event. How many ribbons did they win in all?

___4 × 7 = 28; 28 ribbons___

Multiply Eights

Name _____

Date _____

6 groups of 8 are 48.

6 eights = 48

6 × 8 = 48

$$\begin{array}{r} 8 \\ \times 6 \\ \hline 48 \end{array}$$

Complete each multiplication fact.

1. ___5___ × 8 = __40__

2. 4 × __8__ = 32

3. ___2___ × __8__ = __16__

Write the product.

4. 3 × 8 = __24__   5. 7 × 8 = __56__   6. 6 × 8¢ = __48¢__   7. 8 × 8 = __64__

8. 5 × 8 = __40__   9. 9¢ × 8 = __72¢__   10. 2 × 8 = __16__   11. 1 × 8 = __8__

Multiply.

12. $\begin{array}{r} 8 \\ \times 0 \\ \hline 0 \end{array}$ 13. $\begin{array}{r} 8 \\ \times 9 \\ \hline 72 \end{array}$ 14. $\begin{array}{r} 8¢ \\ \times 8 \\ \hline 64¢ \end{array}$ 15. $\begin{array}{r} 8 \\ \times 7 \\ \hline 56 \end{array}$ 16. $\begin{array}{r} 8 \\ \times 3 \\ \hline 24 \end{array}$ 17. $\begin{array}{r} 8 \\ \times 10¢ \\ \hline 80¢ \end{array}$

18. $\begin{array}{r} 8 \\ \times 4 \\ \hline 32 \end{array}$ 19. $\begin{array}{r} 8 \\ \times 2¢ \\ \hline 16¢ \end{array}$ 20. $\begin{array}{r} 8 \\ \times 6 \\ \hline 48 \end{array}$ 21. $\begin{array}{r} 7 \\ \times 8 \\ \hline 56 \end{array}$ 22. $\begin{array}{r} 8 \\ \times 5 \\ \hline 40 \end{array}$ 23. $\begin{array}{r} 3 \\ \times 8 \\ \hline 24 \end{array}$

Problem Solving

24. Carolyn made 8 puppets on Sunday. During the rest of the week she made 3 times as many puppets. How many puppets did Carolyn make during the rest of the week?

3 × 8 = 24; 24 puppets

Multiply Nines

2 groups of 9 are 18.

2 nines = 18

2 × 9 = 18

$$\begin{array}{r} 9 \\ \times 2 \\ \hline 18 \end{array}$$

Complete each multiplication fact.

1. _____6_____ × 9 = ___54___

2. 3 × ___9___ = ___27___

3. ___5___ × ___9___ = ___45___

Write the product.

4. 0 × 9 = ___0___   5. 4¢ × 9 = ___36¢___   6. 9 × 9 = ___81___   7. 3 × 9 = ___27___

8. 6 × 9¢ = ___54¢___   9. 7 × 9 = ___63___   10. 5 × 9 = ___45___   11. 10 × 9 = ___90___

12. 8 × 9 = ___72___   13. 2 × 9¢ = ___18¢___   14. 9 × 4¢ = ___36¢___   15. 9 × 0 = ___0___

Multiply.

16.
$$\begin{array}{r} 9 \\ \times 2 \\ \hline 18 \end{array}$$

17.
$$\begin{array}{r} 9 \\ \times 4 \\ \hline 36 \end{array}$$

18.
$$\begin{array}{r} 9¢ \\ \times 8 \\ \hline 72¢ \end{array}$$

19.
$$\begin{array}{r} 9 \\ \times 0 \\ \hline 0 \end{array}$$

20.
$$\begin{array}{r} 9 \\ \times 7¢ \\ \hline 63¢ \end{array}$$

21.
$$\begin{array}{r} 9 \\ \times 9 \\ \hline 81 \end{array}$$

Problem Solving

22. Jeanie picked 6 crates of strawberries. Each crate holds 9 pints. How many pints of strawberries did Jeanie pick?

_____6 × 9 = 54; 54 pints_____

Multiply Three Numbers

> Group two factors using this symbol ( ). Then multiply these factors first.
>
> $(3 \times 1) \times 2 = \underline{\ ?\ }$ or $3 \times (1 \times 2) = \underline{\ ?\ }$
>
> $\quad 3 \quad \times 2 = \underline{\ ?\ }$ $3 \times \quad 2 \quad = \underline{\ ?\ }$
>
> $\quad 3 \quad \times 2 = \boxed{6}$ $3 \times \quad 2 \quad = \boxed{6}$

Multiply. Use the grouping shown.

1. $(2 \times 3) \times 1 = \underline{6}$
$\quad \underline{6} \times 1 = \underline{6}$

2. $(3 \times 2) \times 1 = \underline{6}$
$\quad \underline{6} \times 1 = \underline{6}$

3. $(2 \times 4) \times 1 = \underline{8}$
$\quad \underline{8} \times 1 = \underline{8}$

4. $2 \times (3 \times 1) = \underline{6}$
$\quad 2 \times \underline{3} = \underline{6}$

5. $2 \times (4 \times 1) = \underline{8}$
$\quad 2 \times \underline{4} = \underline{8}$

6. $(1 \times 5) \times 3 = \underline{15}$
$\quad \underline{5} \times 3 = \underline{15}$

7. $(4 \times 2) \times 3 = \underline{24}$
$\quad \underline{8} \times 3 = \underline{24}$

8. $(7 \times 1) \times 6 = \underline{42}$
$\quad \underline{7} \times 6 = \underline{42}$

9. $(2 \times 4) \times 5 = \underline{40}$
$\quad \underline{8} \times 5 = \underline{40}$

Write the product. Use any grouping.

10. $3 \times 5 \times 1 = \underline{15}$

11. $2 \times 4 \times 3 = \underline{24}$

12. $3 \times 0 \times 9 = \underline{0}$

13. $8 \times 1 \times 2 = \underline{16}$

14. $3 \times 3 \times 5 = \underline{45}$

15. $4 \times 2 \times 3 = \underline{24}$

16. $2 \times 4 \times 2 = \underline{16}$

17. $6 \times 1 \times 4 = \underline{24}$

18. $5 \times 2 \times 4 = \underline{40}$

19. $5 \times 2 \times 2 = \underline{20}$

20. $8 \times 2 \times 0 = \underline{0}$

21. $4 \times 5 \times 1 = \underline{20}$

22. $3 \times 3 \times 2 = \underline{18}$

23. $1 \times 7 \times 2 = \underline{14}$

24. $6 \times 2 \times 2 = \underline{24}$

Problem Solving

25. There are 3 books on each shelf of the bookcases. Each bookcase has 3 shelves. How many books are there in 4 bookcases? $\underline{4 \times 3 \times 3 = 36;\ 36\ \text{books}}$

Division Review

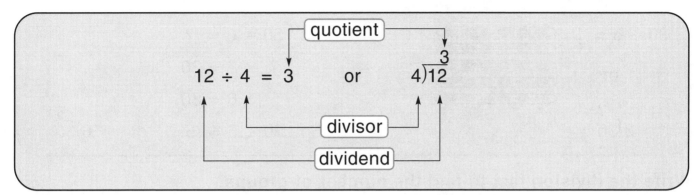

quotient

$$12 \div 4 = 3 \qquad or \qquad 4\overline{)12}^{\,3}$$

divisor

dividend

Divide.

1. $5 \div 1 =$ __5__   **2.** $18 \div 2 =$ __9__   **3.** $12 \div 3 =$ __4__   **4.** $21 \div 3 =$ __7__

5. $2 \div 2 =$ __1__   **6.** $4 \div 4 =$ __1__   **7.** $24 \div 4 =$ __6__   **8.** $35 \div 5 =$ __7__

9. $5\overline{)30}^{\,6}$ **10.** $3\overline{)27}^{\,9}$ **11.** $4\overline{)32}^{\,8}$ **12.** $5\overline{)25}^{\,5}$ **13.** $4\overline{)36}^{\,9}$

14. $4\overline{)20}^{\,5}$ **15.** $5\overline{)45}^{\,9}$ **16.** $3\overline{)24}^{\,8}$ **17.** $4\overline{)16}^{\,4}$ **18.** $5\overline{)40}^{\,8}$

Complete.

19. $21 \div 3 =$ __7__
$7 \times 3 =$ __21__

20. $18 \div 3 =$ __6__
$3 \times$ __6__ $= 18$

21. $30 \div 5 =$ __6__
__6__ $\times 5 = 30$

22. $32 \div$ __4__ $= 8$
__8__ $\times 4 = 32$

23. $16 \div$ __4__ $= 4$
$4 \times$ __4__ $= 16$

24. $0 \div 4 =$ __0__
__0__ $\times 4 = 0$

25. $12 \div 4 =$ __3__
$3 \times 4 =$ __12__

26. $10 \div 2 =$ __5__
$5 \times 2 =$ __10__

27. $36 \div 4 =$ __9__
__9__ $\times 4 = 36$

28. $0 \div 7 =$ __0__
__0__ $\times 7 = 0$

29. $35 \div 5 =$ __7__
__7__ $\times 5 = 35$

30. $45 \div$ __5__ $= 9$
$9 \times$ __5__ $= 45$

Problem Solving

31. Vida's bookcase holds 45 books. If she places her books equally on each of the 5 shelves, how many books are on each shelf?

$45 \div 5 = 9$; 9 books

Use with Lesson 6-7, text pages 200–201.

Divide by 6

Name _____

Date _____

$30 \div 6 = \underline{?}$ (●●●●●●) (●●●●●●) (●●●●●●) (●●●●●●) (●●●●●●)

or

$\underline{}$
$6\overline{)30}$

Think: $30 \div 6 = \underline{?}$

$\underline{?} \times 6 = 30$

$5 \times 6 = 30$

So $30 \div 6 = 5$ or $6\overline{)30}^{\,5}$.

**Write the division fact to find the number of groups.
Then write the related multiplication fact.**

1. (●●●●●●) (●●●●●●)

2. (●●●●●●) (●●●●●●) (●●●●●●) (●●●●●●) (●●●●●●) (●●●●●●) (●●●●●●)

3. (●●●●●●) (●●●●●●) (●●●●●●) (●●●●●●) (●●●●●●) (●●●●●●)

$12 \div \underline{}^{6} = \underline{}^{2}$

$\underline{}^{2} \times \underline{}^{6} = \underline{}^{12}$

$\underline{}^{42} \div \underline{}^{6} = \underline{}^{7}$

$\underline{}^{7} \times \underline{}^{6} = \underline{}^{42}$

$\underline{}^{36} \div \underline{}^{6} = \underline{}^{6}$

$\underline{}^{6} \times \underline{}^{6} = \underline{}^{36}$

Find the quotient. Use counters or skip count to help.

4. $36 \div 6 = \underline{}^{6}$ **5.** $42¢ \div 6 = \underline{}^{7¢}$ **6.** $30 \div 6 = \underline{}^{5}$ **7.** $18 \div 6 = \underline{}^{3}$

8. $54¢ \div 6 = \underline{}^{9¢}$ **9.** $12 \div 6 = \underline{}^{2}$ **10.** $48 \div 6 = \underline{}^{8}$ **11.** $24 \div 6 = \underline{}^{4}$

12. $6\overline{)12}^{\,2}$ **13.** $6\overline{)6¢}^{\,1¢}$ **14.** $6\overline{)54}^{\,9}$ **15.** $6\overline{)48}^{\,8}$ **16.** $6\overline{)18}^{\,3}$

17. $6\overline{)24}^{\,4}$ **18.** $6\overline{)0}^{\,0}$ **19.** $6\overline{)30¢}^{\,5¢}$ **20.** $5\overline{)30}^{\,6}$ **21.** $6\overline{)42}^{\,7}$

Problem Solving

22. Fred collected 48 baseball cards. He had
6 cards of each player. How many players
were pictured in Fred's collection? $48 \div 6 = 8;\ 8\ \text{players}$

Divide by 7

Name _____

Date _____

$$63 \div 7 = \underline{?}$$

or

$$7\overline{)63}^{\,?}$$

Think: $63 \div 7 = \underline{?}$

$\underline{?} \times 7 = 63$

$9 \times 7 = 63$

So $63 \div 7 = 9$ or $7\overline{)63}^{\,9}$.

Write the division fact to find the number of groups.
Then write the related multiplication fact.

1.

$$\underline{35} \div 7 = \underline{5}$$
$$\underline{5} \times \underline{7} = \underline{35}$$

2.

$$\underline{56} \div \underline{7} = \underline{8}$$
$$\underline{8} \times \underline{7} = \underline{56}$$

3.

$$\underline{21} \div \underline{7} = \underline{3}$$
$$\underline{3} \times \underline{7} = \underline{21}$$

Find the quotient. Use counters or skip count to help.

4. $35 \div 7 = \underline{5}$ 5. $63 \div 7 = \underline{9}$ 6. $56 \div 7 = \underline{8}$ 7. $42 \div 7 = \underline{6}$

8. $14¢ \div 7 = \underline{2¢}$ 9. $0 \div 7 = \underline{0}$ 10. $49¢ \div 7 = \underline{7¢}$ 11. $7 \div 7 = \underline{1}$

12. $7\overline{)14}^{\,2}$ 13. $7\overline{)56}^{\,8}$ 14. $7\overline{)49¢}^{\,7¢}$ 15. $7\overline{)0}^{\,0}$ 16. $7\overline{)21}^{\,3}$

17. $7\overline{)28¢}^{\,4¢}$ 18. $4\overline{)28}^{\,7}$ 19. $7\overline{)42}^{\,6}$ 20. $6\overline{)42}^{\,7}$ 21. $1\overline{)7¢}^{\,7¢}$

Problem Solving

22. There are 63 apartments in all. There are 7 apartments on each floor. How many floors are there?

$63 \div 7 = 9$; 9 floors

23. Seven girls grew 21 tomato plants. If each girl grew the same number of plants, how many tomato plants did each girl grow?

$21 \div 7 = 3$; 3 plants

Use with Lesson 6-9, text pages 204–205.

Divide by 8

$72 \div 8 = \underline{?}$

or

$8\overline{)72}^{\,?}$

Think: $72 \div 8 = \underline{?}$

$\underline{?} \times 8 = 72$

$9 \times 8 = 72$

So $72 \div 8 = 9$ or $8\overline{)72}^{\,9}$.

Write the division fact to find the number of groups.
Then write the related multiplication fact.

1.

$40 \div \underline{8} = \underline{5}$
$\underline{5} \times \underline{8} = \underline{40}$

2.

$\underline{24} \div \underline{8} = \underline{3}$
$\underline{3} \times \underline{8} = \underline{24}$

3.

$\underline{32} \div \underline{8} = \underline{4}$
$\underline{4} \times \underline{8} = \underline{32}$

Find the quotient. Use counters or skip count to help.

4. $32 \div 8 = \underline{4}$ 5. $16 \div 8 = \underline{2}$ 6. $64¢ \div 8 = \underline{8¢}$ 7. $56 \div 8 = \underline{7}$

8. $72 \div 8 = \underline{9}$ 9. $48¢ \div 8 = \underline{6¢}$ 10. $8 \div 8 = \underline{1}$ 11. $24 \div 8 = \underline{3}$

12. $8\overline{)40}^{\,5}$ 13. $8\overline{)72}^{\,9}$ 14. $8\overline{)64}^{\,8}$ 15. $8\overline{)8¢}^{\,1¢}$ 16. $8\overline{)16}^{\,2}$

17. $8\overline{)24}^{\,3}$ 18. $4\overline{)48}^{\,6}$ 19. $8\overline{)56¢}^{\,7¢}$ 20. $8\overline{)32}^{\,4}$ 21. $4\overline{)32}^{\,8}$

Problem Solving

22. A bag with 24 crackers is distributed equally among 8 children. How many crackers does each child receive?

$24 \div 8 = 3; \ 3 \text{ crackers}$

23. Ted drives a truck 40 hours a week. If he drives 8 hours a day, how many days does he work each week?

$40 \div 8 = 5; \ 5 \text{ days}$

Divide by 9

Name _____

Date _____

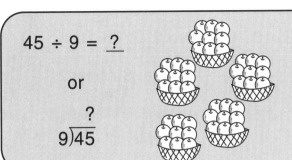

$45 \div 9 = \underline{\ ?\ }$

or

$\begin{array}{r} ? \\ 9{\overline{)45}} \end{array}$

Think: $45 \div 9 = \underline{\ ?\ }$

$\underline{\ ?\ } \times 9 = 45$

$5 \times 9 = 45$

So $45 \div 9 = 5$ or $\begin{array}{r} 5 \\ 9{\overline{)45}} \end{array}$

Write the division fact to find the number of groups.
Then write the related multiplication fact.

1.
$54 \div \underline{\ 9\ } = \underline{\ 6\ }$
$\underline{\ 6\ } \times \underline{\ 9\ } = \underline{\ 54\ }$

2.
$27 \div \underline{\ 9\ } = \underline{\ 3\ }$
$\underline{\ 3\ } \times \underline{\ 9\ } = \underline{\ 27\ }$

3.
$36 \div \underline{\ 9\ } = \underline{\ 4\ }$
$\underline{\ 4\ } \times \underline{\ 9\ } = \underline{\ 36\ }$

Find the quotient. Use counters or skip count to help.

4. $27¢ \div 9 = \underline{\ 3¢\ }$ 5. $63 \div 9 = \underline{\ 7\ }$ 6. $36 \div 9 = \underline{\ 4\ }$ 7. $18 \div 9 = \underline{\ 2\ }$

8. $72 \div 9 = \underline{\ 8\ }$ 9. $45 \div 9 = \underline{\ 5\ }$ 10. $0 \div 9 = \underline{\ 0\ }$ 11. $36¢ \div 9 = \underline{\ 4¢\ }$

12. $\begin{array}{r} 8 \\ 9{\overline{)72}} \end{array}$ 13. $\begin{array}{r} 3 \\ 9{\overline{)27}} \end{array}$ 14. $\begin{array}{r} 4¢ \\ 9{\overline{)36¢}} \end{array}$ 15. $\begin{array}{r} 9 \\ 9{\overline{)81}} \end{array}$ 16. $\begin{array}{r} 1 \\ 9{\overline{)9}} \end{array}$

17. $\begin{array}{r} 2 \\ 9{\overline{)18}} \end{array}$ 18. $\begin{array}{r} 7 \\ 9{\overline{)63}} \end{array}$ 19. $\begin{array}{r} 9 \\ 1{\overline{)9}} \end{array}$ 20. $\begin{array}{r} 6¢ \\ 9{\overline{)54¢}} \end{array}$ 21. $\begin{array}{r} 5 \\ 9{\overline{)45}} \end{array}$

Problem Solving

22. There are 81 packs of light bulbs.
If there are 9 packs per case,
how many cases are there?

$81 \div 9 = 9$; 9 cases

23. There are 18 boys and girls playing a baseball
game. There are 9 players on each team.
How many teams are there?

$18 \div 9 = 2$; 2 teams

Use with Lesson 6-11, text pages 208–209.   73

Operation Patterns

Name _____

Date _____

What number comes next in this pattern? 18, 16, 19, 17, __?__

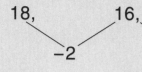 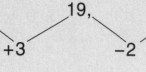

18, ⟍ 16, ⟍ 19, ⟍ 17, ⟍ __?__
   −2   +3   −2   +3

Rule: Subtract 2, Add 3.

18,   16,   19,   17,   __20__   **Think:** 17 + 3 = 20

Complete the pattern. Then write the rule.

1. 25, 22, 19, 16, __13__   Start at 25. −3

2. 1, 2, 3, 6, 7, __14__   Start at 1. ×2; +1

3. 9, 11, 10, 12, 11, 13, __12__   Start at 9. +2; −1

4. 18, 9, 10, 5, 6, __3__   Start at 18. ÷2; +1

5. 23, 18, 24, 19, 25, __20__   Start at 23. −5; +6

6. 1, 8, 2, 16, 4, __32__   Start at 1. ×8; ÷4

Complete each pattern.

7.
$$\begin{array}{r} 8 \\ \times 3 \\ \hline 24 \end{array} \qquad \begin{array}{r} 8 \\ \times 4 \\ \hline 32 \end{array} \qquad \begin{array}{r} 8 \\ \times 5 \\ \hline 40 \end{array} \qquad \begin{array}{r} 8 \\ \times 6 \\ \hline 48 \end{array}$$

8.
$$\begin{array}{r} 9 \\ \times 5 \\ \hline 45 \end{array} \qquad \begin{array}{r} 8 \\ \times 5 \\ \hline 40 \end{array} \qquad \begin{array}{r} 7 \\ \times 5 \\ \hline 35 \end{array} \qquad \begin{array}{r} 6 \\ \times 5 \\ \hline 30 \end{array}$$

9. $6\overline{)54}$ $\;^{9}$ $6\overline{)48}$ $\;^{8}$ $6\overline{)42}$ $\;^{7}$

10. $9\overline{)27}$ $\;^{3}$ $9\overline{)36}$ $\;^{4}$ $9\overline{)45}$ $\;^{5}$

Problem Solving

11. April 4 is on a Sunday. What are the dates of the next two Sundays?

April 11 and April 18

Fact Families; Apply Facts

Name _____

Date _____

These sentences form a fact family for multiplication and division.

Two Multiplication Facts	Two Division Facts
2 × 5 = 10	10 ÷ 5 = 2
[groups] [in each] [in all]	[in all] [in each] [groups]
5 × 2 = 10	10 ÷ 2 = 5

Complete each fact family.

1. 6 × __9__ = 54

__54__ ÷ 9 = 6

9 × __6__ = 54

54 ÷ 6 = __9__

2. __8__ × 3 = 24

24 ÷ __3__ = 8

3 × 8 = __24__

__24__ ÷ 8 = 3

3. 4 × 6 = __24__

24 ÷ __6__ = 4

__6__ × 4 = 24

__24__ ÷ 4 = 6

4. 7 × 8 = __56__

56 ÷ 8 = __7__

__8__ × 7 = 56

56 ÷ __7__ = 8

5. __9__ × 5 = 45

__45__ ÷ 5 = 9

__5__ × 9 = 45

45 ÷ __9__ = 5

6. 3 × __7__ = 21

21 ÷ 7 = __3__

__7__ × 3 = 21

21 ÷ 3 = __7__

Write the complete fact family for each.

7. 2, 9, 18

2 × 9 = 18

18 ÷ 9 = 2

9 × 2 = 18

18 ÷ 2 = 9

8. 4, 5, 20

4 × 5 = 20

20 ÷ 5 = 4

5 × 4 = 20

20 ÷ 4 = 5

9. 3, 6, 18

3 × 6 = 18

18 ÷ 6 = 3

6 × 3 = 18

18 ÷ 3 = 6

Problem Solving

10. Tamika collected 72 coins. She put 8 coins in each holder. How many holders did she use?

72 ÷ 8 = 9; 9 holders

11. Nine students each received 7 stars from the teacher. How many stars did the teacher give to these students?

9 × 7 = 63; 63 stars

Problem-Solving Strategy: Guess and Test

Name _____

Date _____

The sum of two numbers is 9. Their product is 18. What are the two numbers?
Think: $\underline{?} + \underline{?} = 9$; $\underline{?} \times \underline{?} = 18$. Guess and test. Use a table.

Sum	Product
$1 + 8 = 9$	$1 \times 8 = 8$
$2 + 7 = 9$	$2 \times 7 = 14$
$3 + 6 = 9$	$3 \times 6 = 18$

The two numbers are 3 and 6.

Solve. Do your work on a separate sheet of paper.

1. Chris bought a card for 35¢. He gave the clerk 6 coins. What coins did he give the clerk?

   $2 \times 10¢ = 20¢$; $3 \times 5¢ = 15¢$; $20¢ + 15¢ = 35¢$; 2 dimes and 3 nickels

2. The product of two numbers is 36. The sum of the numbers is 13. What are the two numbers?

   $4 \times 9 = 36$; $4 + 9 = 13$; 4 and 9

3. Reid found 6 coins that totaled 61¢ in all. What coins did he find?

   $25¢ + 10¢ + 10¢ + 10¢ + 5¢ + 1¢ = 61¢$; 1 quarter, 3 dimes, 1 nickel, 1 penny

4. The sum of two numbers is 16. The product is 64. Name the numbers.

   $8 + 8 = 16$; $8 \times 8 = 64$; 8 and 8

5. Paul has 30 postcards. He has 4 times as many large postcards as small postcards. How many small postcards does he have? How many large postcards?

   $6 \times 4 = 24$; $24 + 6 = 30$; 6 small; 24 large

6. The quotient of two numbers is 8. The sum of the same two numbers is 72. What are the two numbers?

   $64 \div 8 = 8$; $8 + 8 = 16$; 64 and 8

7. If Angel plants the same number of flowers in each of 5 rows, he will have none left over. If he plants 1 in the first row and then 1 more in each row than he did in the previous row, he will plant flowers in only 4 rows. How many flowers does he have?

   10 flowers

8. Max went to the fair with 5 friends. Some paid $2 each to ride the bumper cars. The rest paid $3 each to ride the roller coaster. They spent $16 in all. How many rode each ride?

   $2 \times \$2 = \$4$; $4 \times \$3 = \$12$; $\$12 + \$4 = \$16$; 4 roller coaster, 2 bumper cars

Problem-Solving
Applications: Mixed Review

Name _____

Date _____

Solve each problem and explain the method you used. If needed, do all your work on a separate sheet of paper.

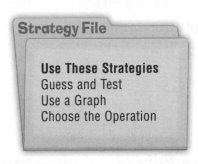

Read ▶ **Plan** ▶ **Solve** ▶ **Check**

Strategy File

Use These Strategies
Guess and Test
Use a Graph
Choose the Operation

1. Connie bought 9 six-packs of soda. How many sodas did she have in all?

9 × 6 = 54; 54 sodas

2. Martin bought 8 pencils at the stationery store. He paid 72¢ total. How much did each pencil cost?

72¢ ÷ 8 = 9; 9¢

3. In each box there are 5 packs of erasers, with 4 erasers in each pack. How many erasers are there in 3 boxes?

5 × 4 = 20; 20 × 3 = 60; 60 erasers

4. Cal bought an apple for 95¢. He used 6 coins to pay for it. What coins might he have used?

25¢ + 25¢ + 25¢ + 10¢ + 5¢ + 5¢ = 95¢; 3 quarters, 1 dime, and 2 nickels

5. There are 24 kids in Mrs. Jones' class. There are twice as many girls as boys. How many boys and girls are there?

8 × 2 = 16; 16 + 8 = 24; 16 girls and 8 boys

Use the chart for problems 6–9.

6. John spent 16¢ on plums. How many did he buy?

16¢ ÷ 8¢ = 2; 2 plums

7. Tighe spent 30¢ on oranges. How many did he buy?

30¢ ÷ 10¢ = 3; 3 oranges

JOE'S FRUIT STAND	
Fruit	**Cost**
Oranges	10¢
Tangerines	9¢
Plums	8¢

8. Laura spent 46¢ on oranges and tangerines. How many did she buy?

9¢ × 4 = 36¢; 1 × 10¢ = 10¢; 36¢ + 10¢ = 46¢; 4 tangerines, 1 orange

9. Jennifer spent exactly 28¢ on fruit. What fruit did she buy?

2 × 10¢ = 20¢; 1 × 8¢ = 8¢; 20¢ + 8¢ = 28¢; 2 oranges and 1 plum

---

Use with Lesson 6-16, text pages 218–219. 77

Pictographs

Name _____

Date _____

Complete the tally chart.

1. The tally chart shows the balloons Zina sold at a parade.

Color	Tally	Total
Red	IIII IIII	10
Blue	IIII I	6
Purple	IIII IIII II	12
Green	IIII	5
Yellow	IIII	4
Silver	IIII III	8

Use the tally chart above to make a pictograph.

Answers may vary. Sample answers given.

2.

Balloons Sold

Red	◯ ◯ ◯ ◯ ◯
Blue	◯ ◯ ◯
Purple	◯ ◯ ◯ ◯ ◯ ◯
Green	◯ ◯ ◗
Yellow	◯ ◯
Silver	◯ ◯ ◯ ◯

Key: Each ◯ = __2__ balloons

3. How many balloons are represented by each symbol?

   Answers will vary.

4. How many balloons did Zina sell in all?

   45

5. Of which color did Zina sell the most balloons? the fewest?

   purple; yellow

6. How many more red balloons than yellow balloons did Zina sell?

   10 − 4 = 6; 6 balloons

7. How many green and silver balloons did Zina sell in all?

   8 + 5 = 13; 13 balloons

8. How many red, blue, and purple balloons did Zina sell in all?

   10 + 6 + 12 = 28; 28 balloons

Bar Graphs

Name _____

Date _____

The tally chart shows one class' favorite animals at the petting zoo.

1. Complete the tally chart.

Animal	Tally	Total
lamb	ЖЖ III	8
kid	ЖЖ ЖЖ	10
calf	ЖЖ	5
colt	ЖЖ ЖЖ II	12
rabbit	ЖЖ ЖЖ IIII	14

Use the tally chart to make a bar graph.

2.

Favorite Animals

Number of Animals (y-axis): 0, 2, 4, 6, 8, 10, 12, 14

lamb   kid   calf   colt   rabbit

Kind of Animal

3. Which animal was the favorite of 12 students?

colt

4. Which animal was liked by twice the number of students who liked the calf?

kid

5. Did more students favor the colt or the rabbit?

rabbit

6. How many students favored the calf and lamb in all?

8 + 5 = 13; 13 students

7. How many more students favored the rabbit than the calf?

14 − 5 = 9; 9 students

8. How many students were in the class?

8 + 10 + 5 + 12 + 14 = 49; 49 students

Surveys

Name _____

Date _____

Use this survey of 15 of John's classmates to complete questions 1–5.

1. Does the data have a mode? If so, what is it?

   _____ yes; 2 _____

2. Which sport is the most popular?

   _____ Soccer _____

3. Write 3 sentences listing some facts about the data.

   _____ Facts will vary. _____

   _____

   _____

Favorite Sport	
Sport	Number of Votes
Football	4
Lacrosse	6
Soccer	7
Basketball	3
Swimming	2
Tennis	2

4. Make a tally chart using the data from the survey.

Favorite Sport	
Football	IIII
Lacrosse	̶I̶H̶T̶ I
Soccer	̶I̶H̶T̶ II
Basketball	III
Swimming	II
Tennis	II

5. Make a pictograph of the data. Have each symbol stand for 2. Symbols will vary.

Favorite Sport	
Football	☺ ☺
Lacrosse	☺ ☺ ☺
Soccer	☺ ☺ ☺ ◖
Basketball	☺ ◖
Swimming	☺
Tennis	☺
Key: Each ☺ = 2 people.	

Circle Graphs

Did $\frac{1}{4}$ of the students prefer fall?
First find the total number of students.
$9 + 3 + 6 + 18 = 36$
Then divide that number by 4.
$\qquad 36 \div 4 = 9$
Yes, $\frac{1}{4}$ of the students prefer fall.

Remember
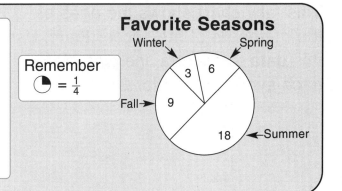 $= \frac{1}{4}$

Favorite Seasons

Use the circle graph at the right to answer questions 1–4.

1. How many students were asked their favorite activity?

   _____ 30 _____

2. Twice as many students preferred bicycle riding to what activity?

   _____ roller skating _____

3. As many students preferred to jump rope as two other activities combined. What are these two activities?

   _____ bicycle riding and roller skating _____

Favorite Activities

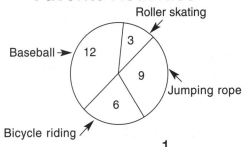

4. Do more or less than $\frac{1}{4}$ of the students prefer baseball?

   _____ more _____

Use the circle graph at the right to answer questions 5–8.

5. Twelve students were asked about their library selections. How many chose science fiction?

   _____ 4 _____

6. What fractional part of the students prefer adventure books?

   _____ $\frac{2}{12}$ or $\frac{1}{6}$ _____

7. Which type of book has the $\frac{1}{3}$ of the readers?

   _____ science fiction _____

Library Selections

8. Which two types of books combined are preferred by half the students?

   _____ nature and mystery, or science fiction and adventure _____

Line Plots

This tally chart shows the ages of the members of the soccer team. Use this data to make a line plot. Make each symbol stand for 2.

Age of Soccer Team Members	
Age	Tally
12	II
13	IIII
14	ЖHI I
15	ЖHI III
16	ЖHI I
17	IIII

1.

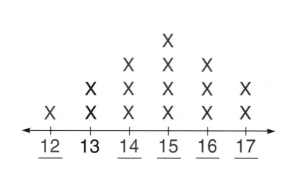

Age of Soccer Team Members

Use the line plot to answer questions 2–7.

2. How many soccer players are older than 13?

_____24_____

3. How many soccer players are either 16 or 17 years old?

_____10_____

4. What is the mode of the soccer players' ages?

_____15_____

5. What is the range of the soccer players' ages?

_____5 years_____

6. What is the total number of soccer players on the team?

_____30_____

7. How many soccer players are older than 17?

_____0_____

Line Graphs

Name _____

Date _____

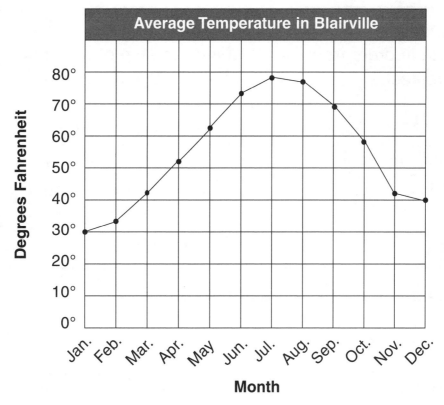

Use the line graph above to answer exercises 1–8.

1. How does the temperature change from February to March? How can you tell?

_____ increase; line goes up _____

2. Does the average temperature increase or decrease between November and December?

_____ decrease _____

3. What is the average temperature for the month of January?

_____ 30°F _____

4. What is the average temperature for the month of December?

_____ 40°F _____

5. Which three months have about the same average temperature?

_____ June, July, and August _____

6. Which month has an average temperature of about 68°F?

_____ September _____

7. Between which two months is the change in temperature the greatest?

_____ October and November _____

8. Does the average temperature increase or decrease from August to September?

_____ decrease _____

Median and Mean

Name _____

Date _____

To find the median:	To find the mean:
Write the data in order from least to greatest.	Find the sum of the data.
	$1 + 2 + 2 + 3 + 4 + 4 + 5 = 21$
1, 2, 2, 3, 4, 4, 5	Divide the sum by the number of items.
Find the *middle* number.	$21 \div 7 = 3$
The median is 3.	sum number of items mean
	The mean is 3.

Find the median and mean for each set of data.

```
        X
  X  X  X
  X  X  X  X        X
  +--+--+--+--+--+--+-->
  1  2  3  4  5  6
```

```
         X        X
  X      X  X  X        X
  +--+--+--+--+--+--+--+-->
  4  5  6  7  8  9  10
```

1. Median: _____ 3

3. Median: _____ 7

2. Mean: _____ 3

4. Mean: _____ 7

```
        X
  X     X     X
  X  X  X  X  X
  +--+--+--+--+-->
  6  7  8  9  10
```

```
        X
        X
        X
  X  X  X  X  X  X
  +--+--+--+--+--+-->
  4  5  6  7  8  9
```

5. Median: _____ 8

7. Median: _____ 5

6. Mean: _____ 8

8. Mean: _____ 6

Compare Data

Name _____

Date _____

Matt and Ruth survey an equal
number of students in different classes,
asking what their favorite color is.
After recording the data, Matt and Ruth
display the results in bar graphs.

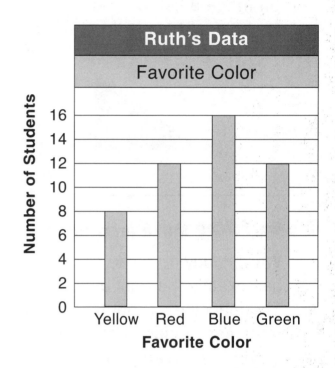

1. Which color was the most
   popular in Ruth's survey?
   in Matt's survey?

   <u>Blue, Red</u>

2. Which color was the least popular
   in Ruth's survey? in Matt's survey?

   <u>Yellow, Green</u>

3. How many students in each class
   were surveyed?

   <u>Ruth: 48, Matt: 46</u>

4. Which person's graph showed a
   greater number of students
   choosing red as a favorite color?

   <u>Matt's</u>

5. How many more people chose
   yellow in Matt's survey than in
   Ruth's survey?

   <u>4</u>

6. How many students in each survey
   chose blue as their favorite color?

   <u>Ruth: 16; Matt:12</u>

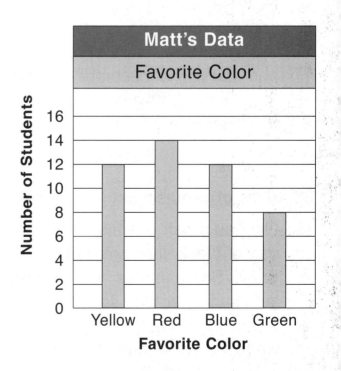

Arrangements and Combinations

Name _____

Date _____

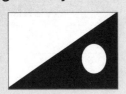

John made a list to show how many ways he could make this flag using the colors green, yellow, and red.

Upper	Lower	
red	green	yellow
red	yellow	green
green	yellow	red
green	red	yellow
yellow	red	green
yellow	green	red

Problem Solving Make an organized list.

1. Ward is buying a can of juice. He has exactly the right change: 35¢. The machine will not take pennies. How many different combinations of coins could Ward have?

Q	Q	D	D	D	N
D	N	D	D	N	N
	N	D	N	N	N
		N	N	N	N
			N	N	N
				N	N
					N

_____ 6 combinations _____

2. Rosie is planting a garden. There are four rows. She wants one row of spinach, two rows of tomatoes, and one row of cucumbers. How many different ways can Rosie plant her garden?

S	T	T	C	T	T	C	S
S	T	C	T	T	T	S	C
S	C	T	T	T	C	T	S
C	T	T	S	T	C	S	T
C	T	S	T	T	S	T	C
C	S	T	T	T	S	C	T

_____ 12 ways _____

Make an organized list and a tree diagram. Check students' lists

3. Lily has a pair of white shoes and a pair of black shoes to go with her dress. She can wear white socks, lace socks, or blue socks with her shoes. How many ways can Lily wear her socks and shoes?

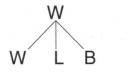

_____ 6 ways _____

Probability Experiments: Events and Outcomes

Name _____

Date _____

> The probability of this spinner landing on blue is 2 out of 7.
>
> The probability of this spinner landing on red is 3 out of 7. So, the chance of landing on red or blue is *not* equally likely.
>
> It is **impossible** that the spinner will land on green. It is **possible** the spinner will land on yellow. It's **certain** the spinner will land on red, blue, or yellow.

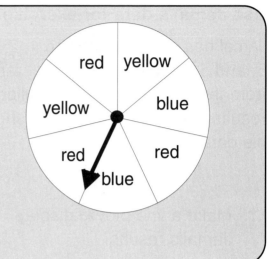

Use the spinner at the right to find the probability of landing on:

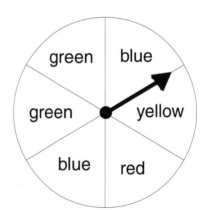

1. green   2 out of 6

2. red   1 out of 6

3. blue   2 out of 6

4. yellow   1 out of 6

Use the spinner below.

5. List the possible outcomes.

red, black, brown, orange

6. Is it more likely that the spinner will land on black or brown? Explain.

black; there are more black sections than brown sections

7. Is it *certain, possible,* or *impossible* that the spinner will land on brown?

possible

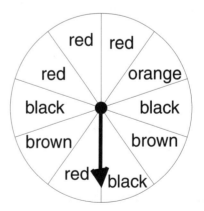

8. Is it *certain, possible,* or *impossible* that the spinner will land on purple?

impossible

9. Is it *certain, possible,* or *impossible* that the spinner will land on black, red, brown or orange?

certain

Graph Results of Probability Experiments

Name _____

Date _____

Use Jamal's data for exercise 1.

Jamal has six cards labeled 1, 2, 3, 4, 5, and 5. He picked a card at random from the pile 18 times and tallied his results. The tally chart below shows his data.

Number	Tally
1	IIII
2	III
3	III
4	II
5	IHI I

1. Make a line plot to display Jamal's results.

2. If Jamal picked another card which card would he most likely pick? Explain your conclusion.

   5; There are more cards labeled 5 than any other.

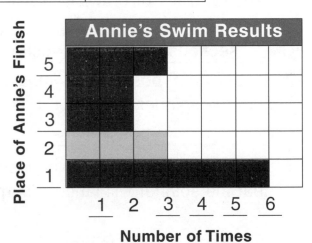

```
                              X
                              X
            X                 X
   X    X   X                 X
   X    X   X   X   X
   X    X   X   X   X
  <---+---+---+---+---+--->
   1   2   3   4   5
       Cards Picked
```

Use Annie's data for exercise 2.

Annie is on the swim team. This tally chart shows the place in which she finished in each of this season's 16 races.

Place	Tally
1	IHI I
2	III
3	II
4	II
5	III

3. Complete the bar graph to display Annie's results.

4. In Annie's next race, is she more likely to come in 5th or 3rd? Explain.

   5th; Annie finished 5th 3 times, 3rd twice

Annie's Swim Results

Place of Annie's Finish / Number of Times

Make Predictions

Name _____

Date _____

- To predict from a line plot, look where the Xs lie.
- Since more Xs are at the beginning of the line plot, you can predict the number of visitors is likely to be between 10 and 29.

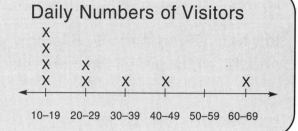

Daily Numbers of Visitors

Use the cards to answer exercises 1–3.

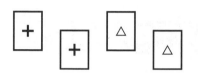

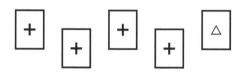

1. What is the probability of picking a card with a plus sign?

   $\frac{6}{10} = \frac{3}{5}$

2. What is the probability of picking a card with a triangle?

   $\frac{4}{10} = \frac{2}{5}$

3. Sally is about to pick a card. Predict which outcome is more likely.

   plus sign

Use the graph to answer exercises 4–7.

Yukio grabbed a handful of mixed nuts from a can. He made a graph to show how many of each kind of nut he grabbed.

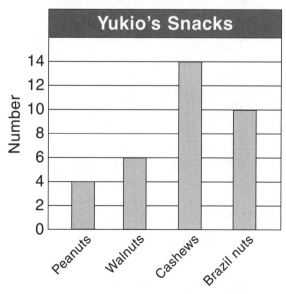

4. Which nut did Yukio have the most of?

   cashews

5. Did Yukio receive more Brazil nuts or walnuts?

   Brazil nuts

6. If Yukio were to grab another handful, predict what kind of nut he would likely get.

   cashew

7. If Yukio were to grab another handful, predict what kind of nut he would be least likely to get.

   peanut

       89

Problem-Solving Strategy: Use a Graph

Name _____

Date _____

How many pencils does Ida have in all?

Ida has 12 red pencils, 8 yellow pencils, and 16 white pencils in her collection.

Ida has 36 pencils.

Pencils in Ida's Collection	
Red	✎ ✎ ✎
Yellow	✎ ✎
White	✎ ✎ ✎ ✎
Key: Each ✎ = 4 pencils.	

Use the bar graph to answer problems 1–3.

1. On which day was the greatest length of trail cleared?

   Thursday

2. How many more feet of trail were cleared Thursday than on Tuesday?

   225 – 150 = 75; 75 feet

3. On which two days were a total of 350 feet of trail cleared?

   Tues. and Sat. or Wed. and Thurs.

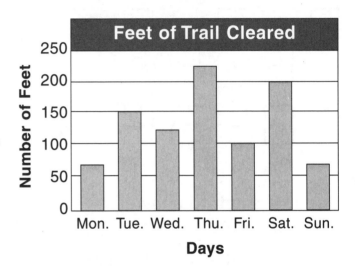

Use the pictograph to answer questions 4–7.

4. On which day were the greatest number of apples sold?

   Tuesday

5. On which day were three times more apples sold than on Friday?

   Thursday

Apples Sold	
Mon.	🍎 🍎 🍎 🍎
Tues.	🍎 🍎 🍎 🍎 🍎 🍎
Wed.	🍎 🍎 🍎 🍎
Thu.	🍎 🍎 🍎 🍎 🍎
Fri.	🍎 🍎
Key: Each 🍎 = 6 apples.	

6. How many symbols would you need to add to increase the number of apples sold on Monday to 48?

   3 more apples

7. What would a half apple represent?

   3 apples

Problem-Solving Applications: Mixed Review

Name _____

Date _____

Solve each problem and explain the method you used. If needed, do all your work on a separate sheet of paper.

Read ▸ Plan ▸ Solve ▸ Check ▸

Use the pictograph for exercises 1–4.

Strategy File

Use These Strategies
Logical Reasoning
Use More Than One Step
Choose the Operation
Guess and Test
Use a Graph

1. Which two grades sold the same amount of wrapping paper?

   <u>first and fourth</u>

2. Which two grades combined to sell 250 rolls of wrapping paper?

   <u>second and fifth</u>

3. Which grade sold the most wrapping paper? by how many rolls?

   <u>third grade; 100 rolls</u>

4. How many rolls of wrapping paper did grades 4 and 5 sell in all?

   <u>200 + 100 = 300; 300 rolls</u>

Grade	Wrapping Paper Sold
1	⬭ ⬭ ⬭ ⬭
2	⬭ ⬭ ⬭
3	⬭ ⬭ ⬭ ⬭ ⬭ ⬭
4	⬭ ⬭ ⬭ ⬭
5	⬭ ⬭

Key: Each ⬭ = 50 rolls of wrapping paper.

Use the bar graph for exercises 5–8.

5. What was the favorite city of the following number of Todd's friends?

   a. 6 <u>Boston</u>

   b. 12 <u>New York</u>

   c. 8 <u>Miami</u>

6. What was the favorite city of more than 9 of Todd's friends?

   <u>New York</u>

7. How many more of Todd's friends picked New York than Boston?

   <u>12 − 6 = 6; 6 more</u>

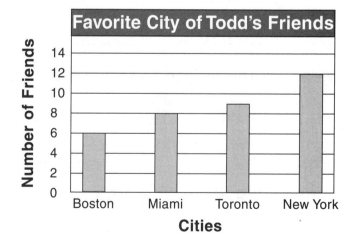

Favorite City of Todd's Friends

8. How many of Todd's friends combined picked Miami, Toronto, and New York?

   <u>8 + 9 + 12 = 29; 29</u>

Quarter Inch, Half Inch, Inch

Name _____

Date _____

> The length of the crayon is *about*:
> - 2 in. to the nearest inch
> - $2\frac{1}{2}$ in. to the nearest half inch
> - $2\frac{1}{4}$ in. to the nearest quarter inch.

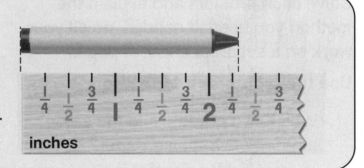

inches

Measure each to the nearest inch, half inch, and quarter inch.

1.

4 in.; $3\frac{1}{2}$ in.; $3\frac{3}{4}$ in.

2.

2 in.; $2\frac{1}{2}$ in.; $2\frac{1}{4}$ in.

Measure the length to the nearest half inch. Check students' work.

3. a book _____

4. an envelope _____

5. a crayon _____

6. a pencil _____

7. a lunch box _____

8. a business card _____

Measure the length to the nearest quarter inch. Check students' work.

9. an eraser _____

10. a finger _____

11. a pen _____

12. a paper clip _____

Draw a line for each length.

13. 5 in. _____

14. $4\frac{1}{2}$ in. _____

15. $2\frac{3}{4}$ in. _____

Foot, Yard

Compare: 10 ft ___?___ 3 yd

1 foot (ft)	= 12 inches (in.)
1 yard (yd)	= 3 feet
1 yard	= 36 inches

ft	3	6	9
yd	1	2	3

9 ft = 3 yd
So 10 ft > 3 yd.

Write the unit used to measure each: in., ft, or yd.

1. the width of a watchband ___in.___

2. the length of a crayon ___in.___

3. the height of a ladder ___ft___

4. the length of a toothbrush ___in.___

5. the length of your arm ___ft___

6. the length of a city block ___yd___

7. the length of the schoolyard ___yd___

8. the height of your kitchen ___ft___

9. the length of a hallway ___yd___

10. the length of a finger ___in.___

Write the letter of the best estimate.

11. the width of a windshield ___a___   **a.** 5 ft   **b.** 5 yd   **c.** 5 in.

12. the width of your math book ___b___   **a.** 8 ft   **b.** 8 in.   **c.** 8 yd

13. the length of your finger ___c___   **a.** 2 yd   **b.** 2 ft   **c.** 2 in.

14. the height of a grandfather clock ___a___   **a.** 6 ft   **b.** 6 yd   **c.** 6 in.

15. the height of a bench ___b___   **a.** 2 in.   **b.** 2 ft   **c.** 2 yd

Compare. Write <, =, or >.

16. 5 yd ___>___ 5 ft   17. 7 in. ___<___ 3 ft   18. 3 ft ___<___ 50 in.

19. 21 ft ___>___ 4 yd   20. 9 yd ___>___ 9 in.   21. 36 in. ___=___ 3 ft

---

Mile

Name _____

Date _____

A mile (mi) is *about* how far you can walk in 25 minutes.

> 1 mi = 5280 ft
> 1 mi = 1760 yd

Which unit would you use to measure each: in., ft, yd, or mi?

1. length of Canada–U.S. border

   _____ mi _____

2. length of a city block

   _____ yd _____

3. length of a dining room table

   _____ ft _____

4. length of your foot

   _____ in. _____

Write the letter of the best estimate.

5. length of a driveway ___b___   **a.** 45 mi   **b.** 45 ft   **c.** 4 mi

6. length of an airport runway ___a___   **a.** 4 mi   **b.** 30 mi   **c.** 300 mi

Compare. Write <, =, >.

7. 1 mi __<__ 1800 yd   **8.** 6000 ft __<__ 2 mi   **9.** 5280 ft __=__ 1 mi

Problem Solving Use the map.

10. What is the shortest distance between Freemont and Brookville?

    41 mi + 26 mi = 67 mi; 67 mi

11. About how far is it to Derby from Ansonia if you go through Charlotte on the way?

    79 mi + 28 mi = 107 mi; 107 mi

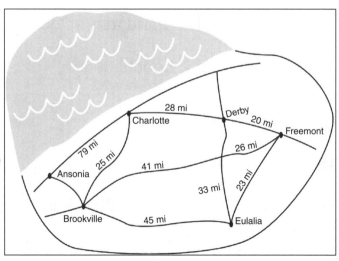

Customary Units of Capacity

Name _____

Date _____

| 1 cup (c) | 1 pint (pt)
1 pt = 2 c | 1 quart (qt)
1 qt = 2 pt | 1 half gallon
1 half gal = 2 qt | 1 gallon (gal)
1 gal = 4 qt |

Which unit is used to measure each: c, pt, qt, or gal?

1. the amount of juice in a large pitcher _____ qt

2. the amount of water in a swimming pool _____ gal

3. the amount of water in a pail _____ gal

4. the amount of milk in a drinking glass _____ c

5. the amount of soup in a bowl _____ c

6. the amount of gas in a car _____ gal

7. the amount of salad oil in a large bottle _____ pt or qt

8. the amount of cider in a jug _____ qt or gal

Compare. Write <, =, or >.

9. 4 qt __>__ 1 half gallon   **10.** 8 pt __<__ 8 qt   **11.** 3 gal __<__ 30 pt

12. 2 qt __=__ 1 half gallon   **13.** 20 c __<__ 25 pt   **14.** 6 pt __<__ 20 c

Complete. You may make a table.

15. 1 qt = __2__ pt   **16.** 3 qt = __6__ pt   **17.** 6 qt = __12__ pt

18. 2 pt = __1__ qt   **19.** 8 pt = __4__ qt   **20.** 5 pt = __10__ c

21. 1 qt = __4__ c   **22.** 5 qt = __20__ c   **23.** 10 pt = __5__ qt

Ounce, Pound

16 oz = 1 lb

About 1 ounce (oz)

About 1 pound (lb)

Which unit is used to measure each: oz or lb?

1. box of cereal __oz__ **2.** motorcycle __lb__ **3.** dictionary __lb__

4. cell phone __oz__ **5.** baseball __oz__ **6.** baseball hat __oz__

Write the letter of the best estimate.

7. canary __c__ **a.** 15 oz **b.** 5 lb **c.** 5 oz

8. ballerina __a__ **a.** 110 lb **b.** 11 oz **c.** 11 lb

9. watermelon __b__ **a.** 18 oz **b.** 8 lb **c.** 1 lb

Compare. Write <, =, or >.

10. 8 oz __<__ 1 lb **11.** 32 oz __=__ 2 lb **12.** 64 oz __<__ 5 lb

13. 1 lb __>__ 12 oz **14.** 80 oz __=__ 5 lb **15.** 112 oz __=__ 7 lb

16. 13 oz __<__ 1 lb **17.** 18 oz __>__ 1 lb **18.** 3 lb __<__ 52 oz

19. 31 lb __>__ 30 oz **20.** 14 oz __<__ 1 lb **21.** 16 oz __=__ 1 lb

Problem Solving

22. Mr. Parker made 4 pounds of potato salad for a party. How many ounces of potato salad did Mr. Parker make?

_____ 4 lb = 64 oz; 64 oz _____

Metric Units of Length

Name _____

Date _____

> Look for benchmarks to help you measure.
>
>
>
> 1 cm
>
> The height of a stack of 6 pennies is about 1 centimeter (cm).
>
> 1 dm
>
>
>
> The length of a cassette is about 1 decimeter (dm).

Which unit is used to measure each: cm or dm?

1. width of a cereal box ___cm___   **2.** height of a poster ___dm___

3. height of a mug ___cm___   **4.** width of a beach towel ___dm___

5. length of a bench ___dm___   **6.** height of a brick ___cm___

Write the letter of the best estimate.

7. length of a rake handle ___a___   **a.** 10 dm   **b.** 10 cm   **c.** 1 dm

8. length of a barrette ___a___   **a.** 8 cm   **b.** 18 cm   **c.** 8 dm

Compare. Write <, =, or >.

9. 20 cm ___=___ 2 dm   **10.** 5 dm ___>___ 10 cm   **11.** 36 cm ___<___ 4 dm

Draw a line for each length. Check students' work.

12. 8 cm

13. 12 cm

14. 1 dm

15. 6 cm

Meter

Name _____

Date _____

> Most doors in your school are probably *about* 1 meter (m) wide.
>
> | 1 m = 100 cm |
> |---|
> | 1 m = 10 dm |

Which unit is used to measure each: cm, dm, or m?

1. length of a windshield wiper <u>dm or cm</u>
2. height of a schoolbus <u>m</u>

3. width of a pie pan <u>cm or dm</u>
4. length of a safety pin <u>cm</u>

5. length of a volleyball net <u>m</u>
6. height of a teacup <u>cm</u>

7. length of a crayon <u>cm</u>
8. length of a boat <u>m</u>

Write the letter of the best estimate.

9. the height of a stack of 10 dimes <u>a</u>   **a.** 1 cm   **b.** 1 m   **c.** 1 dm

10. the thickness of a sandwich <u>b</u>   **a.** 3 m   **b.** 3 cm   **c.** 15 cm

11. the height of a toy rocket ship <u>a</u>   **a.** 4 dm   **b.** 4 m   **c.** 100 m

Compare. Write <, =, or >.

12. 400 cm <u>=</u> 4 m   13. 19 dm <u><</u> 200 cm   14. 30 cm <u><</u> 4 dm

15. 55 cm <u><</u> 6 m   16. 2 m <u>=</u> 20 dm   17. 88 dm <u>></u> 8 m

18. 3 m <u>></u> 30 cm   19. 10 dm <u>=</u> 1 m   20. 40 dm <u>=</u> 4 m

21. 15 dm <u>=</u> 150 cm   22. 7 m <u>></u> 17 dm   23. 501 cm <u>></u> 5 m

Problem Solving

24. A lilac bush grew to a height of 3 m. When it was planted, the bush was 10 dm tall. How much did the lilac bush grow?

3 m = 30 dm;
30 dm − 10 dm = 20 dm or 2 m

Kilometer

A kilometer (km) is *about* how far you can walk in 15 minutes.

| 1 kilometer = 1000 meters |
| 1 km = 1000 m |
| |
| 10 dm = 1 m |
| 10 cm = 1 dm |

Which unit is used to measure each: cm, dm, m or km?

1. length of a rowboat _____ m _____ **2.** height of a tree _____ m _____

3. length of a bread knife ___ cm or dm ___ **4.** distance across an ocean ___ km ___

5. length of toothbrush ___ cm or dm ___ **6.** width of window _____ dm _____

7. distance from home to school ___ m or km ___ **8.** length of classroom _____ m _____

Compare. Write <, =, or >.

9. 2 km __=__ 2000 m   **10.** 1800 dm __>__ 10 m   **11.** 2700 cm __=__ 27 m

Problem Solving

12. What is the shortest distance in kilometers from the Base Camp to the Summit Camp?

_____ 3 km + 3 km = 6 km; 6 km _____

13. Miranda and Kate started at Base Camp and walked halfway to the Summit Camp for a picnic. How many kilometers did they walk?

_____ 3 km _____

14. In the afternoon Kate and Miranda joined Robin in a hike from Picnic Spot to Eagle Rock, then on to Summit Camp. How many kilometers did they hike after lunch?

_____ 4 km + 3 km = 7 km; 7 km _____

Milliliter, Liter

Name _____

Date _____

1 liter = 1000 milliliters
1 L = 1000 mL

1 milliliter (mL)   1 liter (L)

**Write *less than a liter*, *about 1 liter*, or *more than a liter*
for the amount of liquid each real object holds.**

1.

more than a liter

2.

about 1 liter

3.

less than 1 liter

4.

less than a liter

5.

about 1 liter

6.

more than 1 liter

Which unit is used to measure each: mL or L?

7. liquid medicine ___mL___   8. carton of milk ___L___

9. water in a bathtub ___L___   10. juice in a baby's bottle ___mL___

Write the letter of the best estimate.

11. syrup for 2 pancakes ___a___   **a.** 25 mL **b.** 2 mL **c.** 2 L

12. water in a rain barrel ___c___   **a.** 75 mL **b.** 7 L **c.** 75 L

Compare. Write <, =, or >.

13. 3640 mL __>__ 3 L **14.** 4 L __<__ 8000 mL **15.** 1 L __=__ 1000 mL

100   **Use with Lesson 8-9, text pages 276–277.**

Gram, Kilogram

Name _____

Date _____

1 kilogram = 1000 grams
1 kg = 1000 g

1 gram (g)   1 kilogram (kg)

Write *more than a kilogram, about a kilogram,* or *less than a kilogram* for the mass of each real object.

1.

less than a kilogram

2.

less than a kilogram

3.

more than a kilogram

4.

about a kilogram

5.

more than a kilogram

6.

less than a kilogram

Which unit is used to measure each: g or kg?

7. paper clip ___g___   **8.** tent ___kg___   **9.** butter for toast ___g___

Write the letter of the best estimate.

10. medium-sized adult dog ___b___   **a.** 14 g   **b.** 14 kg   **c.** 140 kg

11. small paper bag ___a___   **a.** 20 g   **b.** 20 kg   **c.** 2 kg

12. car ___a___   **a.** 1000 kg   **b.** 100 kg   **c.** 100 g

13. math book ___b___   **a.** 50 g   **b.** 1 kg   **c.** 5 kg

Compare. Write <, =, or >.

14. 4000 g __<__ 40 kg   **15.** 2 kg __=__ 2000 g   **16.** 3300 g __>__ 3 kg

Rename Units of Measure

Name _____

Date _____

To rename a larger unit as a smaller unit, multiply.	To rename a smaller unit as a larger unit, divide.
4 dm = __?__ cm	4 pt = __?__ qt
Think: 1 dm = 10 cm	**Think:** 2 pt = 1 qt
4 × 10 = 40	4 ÷ 2 = 2
So, 4 dm = 40 cm.	4 pt = 2 qt

Rename each unit of measure.

1. 20 cm = __2__ dm   **2.** 6 c = __3__ pt   **3.** 6 pt = __12__ c

4. 6 pt = __3__ qt   **5.** 10 dm = __1__ m   **6.** 12 qt = __3__ gal

7. 3 gal = __12__ qt   **8.** 8 qt = __16__ pt   **9.** 2 dm = __20__ cm

Compare. Write <, =, or >.

10. 2 dm __=__ 20 cm   **11.** 110 dm __>__ 1 m   **12.** 2 qt __<__ 5 pt

13. 10 m __>__ 90 dm   **14.** 3 gal __<__ 14 qt   **15.** 36 ft __=__ 12 yd

16. 17 qt __>__ 4 gal   **17.** 2 dm __<__ 21 m   **18.** 4 m __<__ 50 dm

Problem Solving

19. Cody can jump up 38 inches on the trampoline. Caroline can jump up a yard. Who can jump higher?

1 yd = 36 in.; 36 in. < 38 in.; Cody

20. Martha needs 20 gallons of mineral water to fill her fish tank. The store sells mineral water by the quart. How many quarts of water should she buy to fill the tank?

1 gal = 4 qt; 20 × 4 = 80; 80 qt

Choose the
Measuring Tool

Name _____

Date _____

Measuring Tools

meterstick	yardstick
ruler (in.)	ruler (cm)
balance	scale
cup	liter
gallon	tape measure

Write the tool you would use to measure each.

1. mass of a pumpkin

_____balance or scale_____

2. height of a mouse

_____ruler (in. or cm)_____

3. amount of oil in a tanker

_____gallon or liter_____

4. width of a bed

_____meterstick, yardstick, or tape measure_____

Match each object with the tool you would use to find each measure.

5. weight of an apple	_____d_____		**a.**	meterstick
6. height of a picture frame	_____c_____		**b.**	gallon
7. length of a porch	_____a_____		**c.**	inch ruler
8. water in a park fountain	_____b_____		**d.**	scale

Name two things you can measure with each: Answers may vary.
Sample answers given.

9. meterstick or yardstick

_____length of a room_____

_____height of a desk_____

10. inch ruler or centimeter ruler

_____width of a nickel_____

_____length of a paintbrush_____

11. liter or gallon

_____water in a fish tank_____

_____water in a swimming pool_____

Use with Lesson 8-12, text pages 282–283.

Temperature

Name _____

Date _____

	Celsius (°C)	Fahrenheit (°F)
Normal body temperature	37°C	98.6°F
Water freezes	0°C	32°F
Water boils	100°C	212°F

Write the letter of the most reasonable temperature.

1. hot cider   __a__   **a.** 125°F   **b.** 25°F   **c.** 45°F

2. snowball   __b__   **a.** 32°C   **b.** ⁻5°C   **c.** 50°C

3. room in a house   __c__   **a.** 100°C   **b.** 1°C   **c.** 20°C

Answer Yes or No.

4. The bath water is 95°C. Is it just right for a bath?

   _____ No _____

5. The temperature in the house is 68°C. Are you comfortable?

   _____ No _____

6. The school nurse takes your temperature. It is 101°F. Do you have a fever?

   _____ Yes _____

7. The temperature outside is 10°C. Could it snow today?

   _____ No _____

Write each temperature.

8.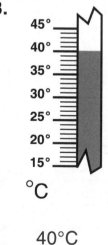

   °C

   __40°C__

9.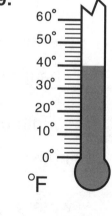

   °F

   __40°F__

10.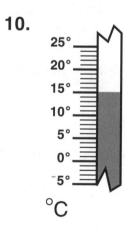

    °C

    __15°C__

Quarter Hour

standard form: 4:15
four fifteen
quarter past four
quarter after four

standard form: 4:30
four thirty
half past four
30 minutes after four

standard form: 4:45
four forty-five
quarter to five

Write each time in standard form.

1.

8:00

2.

12:15

3.

7:30

4.

5:15

5.

2:45

6.

11:30

7.

5:45

8.

12:30

Write the time in words. Use A.M. or P.M. Words may vary.

9.  Go to Bed

quarter after eight P.M.

10.  School Ends

three o'clock P.M.

11.  Eat Lunch

quarter to twelve A.M.

12.  Dinner Time

half past six P.M.

Use with Lesson 8-14, text pages 286–287. 105

Minutes

Name _____

Date _____

5 minutes after 12   30 minutes after 12   38 minutes after 12
55 minutes before 1   30 minutes before 1   22 minutes before 1

Write each time.

1.

_20_ minutes after _11_

_40_ minutes before _12_

2.

_9_ minutes after _8_

_51_ minutes before _9_

3.

_48_ minutes after _10_

_12_ minutes before _11_

Write the time in standard form.

4. 22 minutes before 11

_10_ : _38_

5. 13 minutes after 1

_1_ : _13_

6. 5 minutes before 4

_3_ : _55_

7. 30 minutes before 5

_4_ : _30_

8. 1 minute after 10

_10_ : _01_

9. 35 minutes after 3

_3_ : _35_

Draw the time. Show the hour and the minute hands. Check students' work.

10. 12:48

11. 10:21

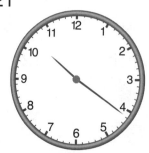

12. 3:50

Elapsed Time

Name _____

Date _____

How much time does the trip take?

Bus Departs	7:10
Bus Arrives	9:30

You can skip count minutes by 5 or 10. You can count hours by 1s first.

7:10
8:10   1 hour
9:10   2 hours
9:20   10 minutes
9:30   20 minutes

This trip takes 2 hours, 20 minutes.

What time will it be in 20 minutes if it is now:

1. 2:10 ___2:30___   **2.** 8:15 ___8:35___   **3.** 7:35 ___7:55___

What time will it be in 3 hours?

4. 5:55 ___8:55___   **5.** 1:05 ___4:05___   **6.** 10:40 ___1:40___

What time will it be in 2 hours, 15 minutes?

7. 6:30 ___8:45___   **8.** 3:35 ___5:50___   **9.** 4:25 ___6:40___

Find the elapsed time.

10. 11:15 A.M.
12:30 P.M.

___1 h 15 min___

11. 2:40 P.M.
8:40 P.M.

___6 h___

12. 11:25 P.M.
2:00 A.M.

___2 h 35 min___

Problem Solving Use the schedule.

13. How long does it take to go from Lakeland to Grove City?

___1 h 25 min___

14. Between what two places will the passengers be at 2:30 P.M.?

___Rockdale and N. Orange___

Schedule of Bus Stops	
Bolton	12:25 P.M.
Rockdale	1:10 P.M.
N. Orange	2:40 P.M.
S. Orange	2:55 P.M.
Lakeland	3:20 P.M.
Libertad	3:45 P.M.
Grove City	4:45 P.M.

Calendar

Name _____

Date _____

April 2009						
Sun.	Mon.	Tues.	Wed.	Thurs.	Fri.	Sat.
			1	2	3	4
5	6	7	8	9	10	11
12	13	14	15	16	17	18
19	20	21	22	23	24	25
26	27	28	29	30		

1 week (wk) = 7 days (d)
1 year (yr) = 365 days
  52 weeks
  12 months (mo)
1 leap year = 366 days

The date of the last day of the month can be written two ways: April 30, 2009 or 4/30/09.

Use the calendar above for exercises 1–4.

1. April has _____30_____ days.   2. A leap year has _____366_____ days.

3. Give the date for:

   a. the second Saturday _April 11_   **b.** the second day _____April 2_____

   c. the last Monday _April 27_   **d.** the fifth Thursday _April 30_

   e. the third
   Tuesday _April 21_   **f.** the first Sunday of
   the month _April 5_

4. Give the day of the week for:

   a. April 21 _____Tuesday_____   **b.** April 25 _____Saturday_____

   c. April 2 _____Thursday_____   **d.** May 1 _____Friday_____

   e. 1 week after April 6 _Monday_   **f.** next to last day _Wednesday_

Write each date two ways. Check students' work.

5. tomorrow's date   6. the last day of this month

   _____   _____

   _____   _____

Problem-Solving
Strategy: Make a Table

Name _____

Date _____

Each soccer team has 14 players. The tournament has 6 teams. How many players are in the tournament in all?

Teams	1	2	3	4	5	6
Players	14	28	42	56	70	84

84 players will play in the tournament.

Solve. Do your work on a separate sheet of paper.

1. Sandy has 28 pairs of shoes in her closet. How many shoes does Sandy have in her closet in all?

   56 shoes

2. Mariana has six bracelets. Each bracelet has 12 beads. How many beads are on the bracelets in all?

   72 beads

3. Paul bought 8 packs of baseball cards. Each pack contained 9 cards. How many baseball cards did Paul buy in all?

   72 cards

4. Jack buys a sandwich for lunch every day. Each sandwich costs $6.00. How much does Jack spend on sandwiches in one week?

   $42.00

5. A grand slam in baseball scores 4 runs. If Albert hits 5 grand slams, how many runs are scored in all?

   20 runs

6. It takes 12 gallons of gas to fill Vinny's car. If gas is $3.00 a gallon, how much does it cost to fill Vinny's car?

   $36.00

7. Timmy needs to replace all the tires on the four cars in his garage. How many tires must Timmy replace in all?

   16 tires

8. Each volleyball team has 18 players. If there are 5 teams in the league, how many players are in the league in all?

   90 players

Problem-Solving Applications: Mixed Review

Name _____

Date _____

Solve each problem and explain the method you used. If needed, do all your work on a separate sheet of paper.

Read ▶ Plan ▶ Solve ▶ Check ▶

Strategy File

Use These Strategies
Use More Than One Step
Draw a Picture
Logical Reasoning
Make a Table

1. Jojo's hamburger shop serves 8 ounce hamburgers. If Jojo expects to sell 50 hamburgers Friday night, how many pounds of meat does he need?

   8 oz × 50 = 400 oz; 1 lb = 16 oz;
   400 oz ÷ 16 = 25; 25 lb

2. Marco filled up his swimming pool with a hose. The hose poured 7 quarts per minute. How many gallons were in the pool after 4 minutes?

   7 qt × 4 = 28 qt; 1 gal = 4 qt;
   28 ÷ 4 = 7; 7 gallons

3. The temperature was 75°F at 11 P.M. 6 hours earlier the temperature was 17 degrees cooler. What were the time and temperature of the earlier measure?

   58°F at 5 P.M.

4. Gina's car is 3 yards long. Louis's car is 15 feet long. Who has the longer car? By how many feet?

   1 yd = 3 ft; 3 × 3 = 9 ft; 9 ft < 15 ft;
   15 − 9 = 6; Louis, 6 ft

5. Connor's family produces 8 ounces of trash each day. How many ounces of trash do they produce in 3 weeks?

   8 × 7 = 56; 56 × 3 = 168;
   168 ounces

6. Chino's birthday is one week after his parents' anniversary. If the date of the anniversary is August 1, on what date is Chino's birthday?

   August 8

7. Niqui rode a bike on vacation. He rode 2 km on the first day and 3 km on the second day. How many meters did Niqui ride in all?

   3 + 2 = 5; 5 × 1000 = 5000;
   5000 meters

8. Each football player has a 5 quart water bottle for practices. How many pints are in each bottle?

   5 × 2 = 10; 10 pints

9. Roy ate lunch, then took a nap at 2 o'clock. When he woke an hour later, was it 3 A.M. or 3 P.M.?

   3 P.M.

Lines

Name _____

Date _____

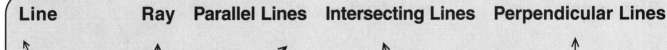

| Line | Ray | Parallel Lines | Intersecting Lines | Perpendicular Lines |

Line Segment

Name each: line, line segment, ray, or none of these.

1.

line segment

2.

line

3.

line segment

4.

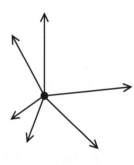

rays

5.

none of these

6.

rays

7.

ray

8.

line

Draw a line that: Answers may vary.

9. is parallel to the line.

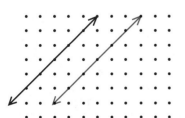

10. intersects the line.

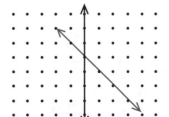

11. is perpendicular to the line.

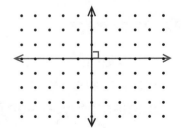

Angles

Name _____

Date _____

Right Angles	Angles
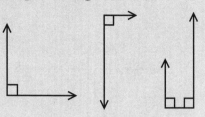	 acute angle obtuse angle less than a greater than a right angle right angle

How many angles does each figure have?

1.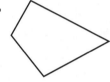

     4

2.

     3

3.

     4

4.

     6

How many right angles does each figure have?

5.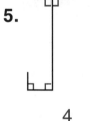

     4

6.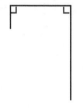

     2

7.

     4

8.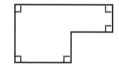

     5

Tell if the angle is a *right angle,* an *acute angle,* or an *obtuse angle.*

9.

     acute angle

10.

     right angle

11.

     obtuse angle

12.

     acute angle

Problem Solving

13. Look at the picture.
    How many right
    angles do you see?

     13

Polygons and Circles

Name _____

Date _____

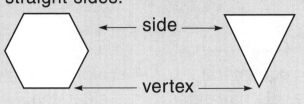

Write the number of sides and vertices for each.

1.

Sides ___0___
Vertices ___0___

2.

Sides ___3___
Vertices ___3___

3.

Sides ___4___
Vertices ___4___

4.
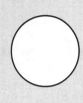
Sides ___6___
Vertices ___6___

5.

Sides ___4___
Vertices ___4___

6.

Sides ___5___
Vertices ___5___

7.

Sides ___8___
Vertices ___8___

8.
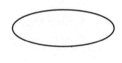
Sides ___0___
Vertices ___0___

Is each figure a polygon? Write *Yes* or *No*.

9.
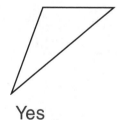
___Yes___

10.

___Yes___

11.
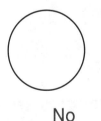
___No___

12.
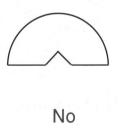
___No___

Draw a polygon. Answer the question. Drawing may vary.

13. 4 sides

14. 6 vertices

How many vertices? ___4___   How many sides? ___6___

Triangles

Triangles are polygons with three sides.

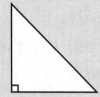 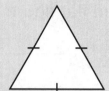

A right triangle has one right angle.

An isosceles has at least two sides of equal length.

An equilateral triangle has sides that are all equal in length.

A scalene triangle has sides that are all different in length.

Name each triangle.

1.

isosceles
triangle

2.
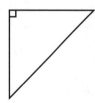
right
triangle

3.

scalene
triangle

4.
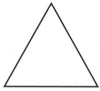
equilateral
triangle

5.

scalene
triangle

6.
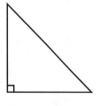
right
triangle

7.

equilateral
triangle

8.

isosceles
triangle

Write how many acute angles are in each triangle.

9.
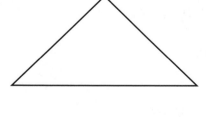
2

10.
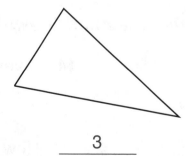
3

11.
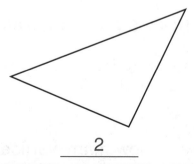
2

Congruent and Similar Figures

Name _____

Date _____

Congruent Figures same shape and size	**Similar Figures** same shape, different size
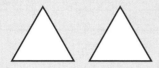	

Do the pairs look congruent? Write _Yes_ or _No._

1.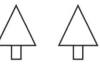

Yes

2.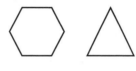

No

3.

No

Do the pairs look similar? Write _Yes_ or _No._

4.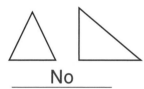

No

5.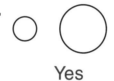

Yes

6.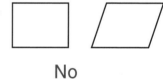

No

Draw a congruent figure for each. Answers may vary.

7.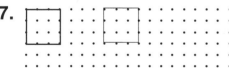

8.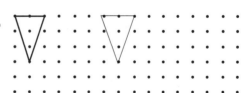

9.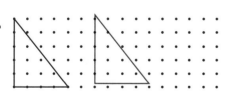

10.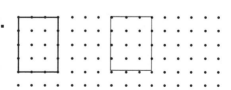

Draw a similar figure for each. Answers may vary.

11.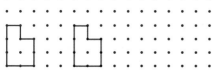

12.

Ordered Pairs

Name _____

Date _____

Look at the graph below. What picture is at the point (5, 6)? Begin at 0. Move 5 spaces to the right. Move 6 spaces up. The trees are located at (5, 6).

Use the graph. Write the place for each ordered pair.

1. (6, 9) ___Fort Kent___

2. (4, 2) ___Portland___

3. (5, 5) ___Millinocket___

4. (8, 3) ___Bar Harbor___

5. (0, 3) ___Bethel___

6. (9, 5) ___Calais___

7. (2, 1) ___Sanford___

8. (7, 8) ___Presque Isle___

9. (2, 5) ___Greenville___

10. (3, 3) ___Augusta___

11. (3, 7) ___Mount Katahdin___

12. (5, 0) ___Kittery___

13. (1, 8) ___Jackman___

14. (8, 7) ___Houlton___

15. (5, 4) ___Bangor___

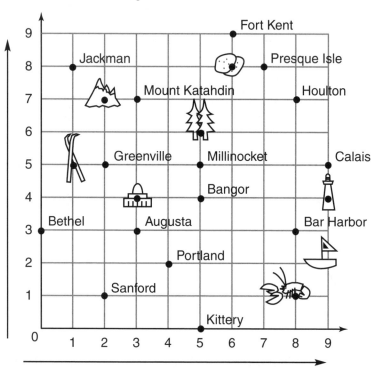

Write the ordered pair for each picture on the graph.

16. mountain ___(2, 7)___

17. lighthouse ___(9, 4)___

18. potatoes ___(6, 8)___

19. skis ___(1, 5)___

20. sailboat ___(9, 2)___

21. lobster ___(8, 1)___

Symmetry

The dashed lines are lines of symmetry.

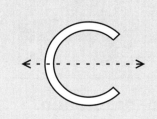 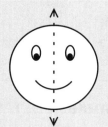 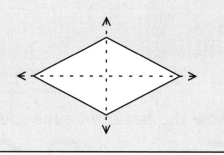

Is the dashed line a line of symmetry? Write Yes or No.

1.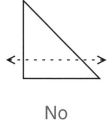

No

2.

No

3.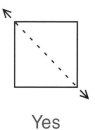

Yes

4.

No

5.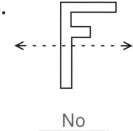

No

6.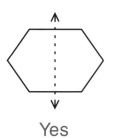

Yes

7.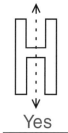

Yes

8.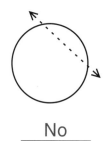

No

Draw a line of symmetry through each figure.

9.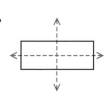

10.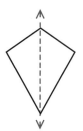

11.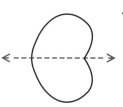

12.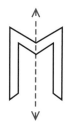

Draw capital letters that have two lines of symmetry. Answers may vary.
Sample answers given.

13.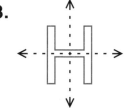

14.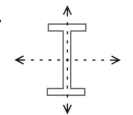

15.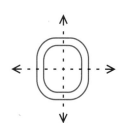

16.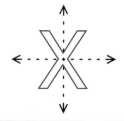

Transformations

Name _____

Date _____

Translation	Reflection	Rotation

Write how the letter was moved: translation, reflection, or rotation.

1.

rotation

2.

reflection

3.

rotation

4.

translation

5.

translation

6.

reflection

7.

rotation

8.

translation

Identify the move.

9.

reflection

10.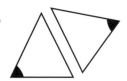

rotation

11.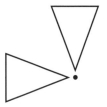

rotation

12.

rotation

13.

translation

14.

rotation

15.

translation

16.

reflection

Solid Figures

Name _____

Date _____

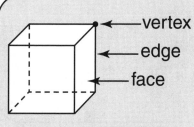 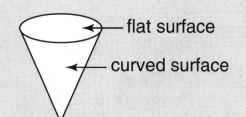

vertex
edge
face

flat surface
curved surface

A cube has 6 faces,
12 edges,
8 vertices.

A cone has 1 flat surface,
1 curved surface,
0 faces,
0 edges,
0 vertices.

Remember: Some solid figures do not have faces, edges, and vertices because they do not have line segments.

Write the number of faces, edges, and vertices.

1.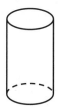

Faces ___5___

Edges ___8___

Vertices ___5___

2.

Faces ___0___

Edges ___0___

Vertices ___0___

3.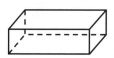

Faces ___6___

Edges ___12___

Vertices ___8___

4.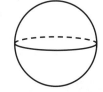

Faces ___0___

Edges ___0___

Vertices ___0___

Name the space figure formed by folding each net.

5.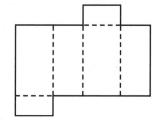

___rectangular prism___

6.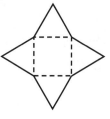

___(square) pyramid___

7.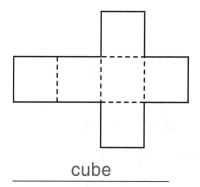

___cube___

Problem Solving

8. I am a space figure with 5 faces, 8 edges, and 4 corners. Which space figure am I?

___triangular pyramid___

Perimeter

Name _____

Date _____

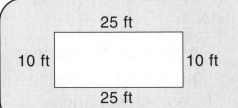

To find the perimeter of a figure,
add the lengths of its sides.

Perimeter = 25 ft + 10 ft + 25 ft + 10 ft
Perimeter = 70 ft.

Write the perimeter.

1.
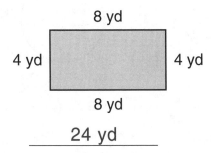

3 m

4 m

5 m

6 m

__18 m__

2.
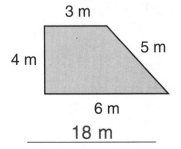

5 ft

5 ft

5 ft

5 ft

__20 ft__

3.
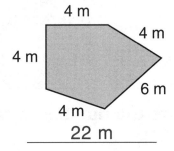

4 m

4 m

4 m

4 m

6 m

__22 m__

4.
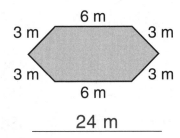

8 yd

4 yd

4 yd

8 yd

__24 yd__

5.
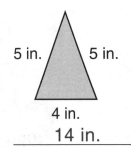

5 in.

5 in.

4 in.

__14 in.__

6.
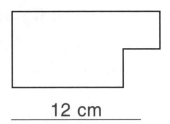

6 m

3 m

3 m

3 m

3 m

6 m

__24 m__

Use your centimeter ruler to find the perimeter of each.

7.
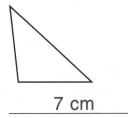

__7 cm__

8.
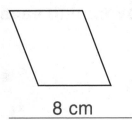

__8 cm__

9.
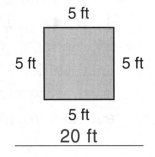

__12 cm__

Problem Solving

10. Matt has a square picture that measures
10 cm on a side. What is the perimeter
of the picture?

10 + 10 + 10 + 10 = 40;
40 cm

11. What is the perimeter of a clock in the shape
of a hexagon if each side measures 9 in.?

9 + 9 + 9 + 9 + 9 + 9 = 54;
54 in.

Area

Name _____

Date _____

□ | ▯ | ⊞

1 square unit   2 square units   6 square units

Write the area.

1.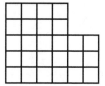

26 square units

2.

6 square units

3.

8 square units

4.

16 square units

5.

7 square units

6.

10 square units

7.

9 square units

8.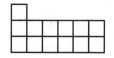

11 square units

9.

9 square units

Problem Solving

You may draw a picture.

10. The Johnsons' living room rug is
3 square units wide and 4 square units long.
What is the area of the rug?

$3 \times 4 = 12$;
12 square units

11. Bill's bedroom floor is 9 square units long
and 8 square units wide. What is its area?

$9 \times 8 = 72$;
72 square units

Volume

The volume of a space figure is the number of cubic units it contains.

1 cubic
unit

Volume =
4 cubic units

Volume =
8 cubic units

Find the volume in cubic units.

1.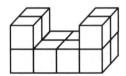

_____ 12 cubic units _____

2.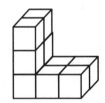

_____ 10 cubic units _____

3.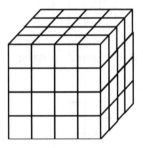

_____ 64 cubic units _____

4.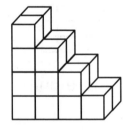

_____ 20 cubic units _____

5.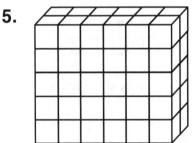

_____ 60 cubic units _____

6.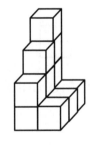

_____ 12 cubic units _____

Problem Solving

7. How many cubic units are needed to make
the figure in exercise 1 a rectangular prism?

_____ 4 cubic units _____

Problem-Solving Strategy: Solve a Simpler Problem

Name _____

Date _____

Solve each problem and explain the method you used. If needed, do all your work on a separate sheet of paper.

Solve a simpler problem first to solve each problem.
Use the design at right to solve exercises 1–3.

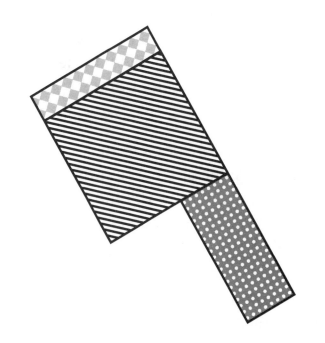

1. Yanna made this design. If the checkerboard rectangle has an area of 5 square units, what is the area of the polka dot rectangle?

   <u>   10 square units   </u>

2. What is the area of the striped rectangle?

   <u>   25 square units   </u>

3. What is the area of the whole design?

   <u>   40 square units   </u>

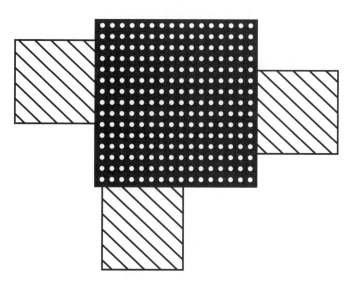

Use the design at left to solve exercises 4–6.

4. Becky made this design. If the striped squares have an area of 4 square units each, what is the total area of the striped squares?

   <u>   12 square units   </u>

5. What is the area of the polka dot square?

   <u>   16 square units   </u>

6. What is the area of the whole design?

   <u>   28 square units   </u>

Problem-Solving Applications: Mixed Review

Solve each problem and explain the method you used. If needed, do all your work on a separate sheet of paper.

Read ▸ Plan ▸ Solve ▸ Check ▸

Strategy File

Use These Strategies
Logical Reasoning
Guess and Test
Choose the Operation
Solve a Simpler Problem
Draw a Picture

1. Nestor has a rectangular vegetable garden. Two of the sides are 8 meters long. The other sides are 6 meters long. What is the perimeter of Nestor garden?

   8 + 8 + 6 + 6 = 28 meters

2. Conan uses cubes to make a rectangular prism. The prism has 4 layers, and the volume of the figure is 16 cubic units. How many cubes are in each layer?

   16 ÷ 4 = 4; 4 cubes

3. Antonio's bedroom is 12 feet long and 8 feet wide. Trudy's bedroom is 10 feet long and 10 feet wide. Whose room has the greatest area? By how many feet?

   12 × 8 = 96; 10 × 10 = 100;
   100 > 96; Trudy; 100 − 96 = 4; 4 ft

4. Cindy's trampoline has 8 sides. Each side is 2 feet long. What is the perimeter of the trampoline?

   2 × 8 = 16; 16 ft.

5. Frank has a rectangular carpet with an area of 42 ft². If both sides of the carpet are more than 5 ft, what are the lengths of the two sides?

   6 × 7 = 42; 6 ft, 7 ft

6. The Robinson's van has 3 rows of seats and 3 seats in each row. If all 7 members of the family are in the van, how many empty seats are there?

   3 × 3 = 9; 9 − 7 = 2; 2 empty seats

7. Jeremy draws an equilateral triangle. If he draws a line of symmetry that creates two triangles, what kind of triangles are they?

   right triangles

8. Ray, Maria, and Paul have a circle, a hexagon and a cube. Maria's figure has no vertices. Paul's figure has a volume of 8 cm³. Which person has which figure?

   Ray—hexagon, Maria—circle, Paul—cube

9. Millen has two paintings on the wall. One is 3 ft tall and 2 ft wide. The second is 4 ft tall and 3 ft wide. What is the total area of the two paintings?

   3 × 2 = 6; 4 × 3 = 12; 12 + 6 = 18;
   18 sq. ft

Multiplication Patterns

Name _____

Date _____

4 × 6 = 24 4 × 60 = 240 4 × 600 = 2400 4 × 6000 = 24,000	• Write the product of the basic fact. • Count the number of zeros in the factors. • Then write the same number of zeros in the product.

Use a basic fact and patterns to find each product.

1. 5 × 6 = _30_

5 × 60 = _300_

5 × 600 = _3000_

5 × 6000 = _30,000_

2. 3 × 8 = _24_

3 × 80 = _240_

3 × 800 = _2400_

3 × 8000 = _24,000_

3. 4 × 7 = _28_

4 × 70 = _280_

4 × 700 = _2800_

4 × 7000 = _28,000_

4. 9 × 2 = _18_

9 × 20 = _180_

9 × 200 = _1800_

9 × 2000 = _18,000_

5. 4 × 9 = _36_

4 × 90 = _360_

4 × 900 = _3600_

4 × 9000 = _36,000_

6. 6 × 7 = _42_

6 × 70 = _420_

6 × 700 = _4200_

6 × 7000 = _42,000_

Find each product.

7. 4 × 300 = _1200_

8. 5 × 200 = _1000_

9. 7 × 2000 = _14,000_

10. 6 × 70 = _420_

11. 7 × 400 = _2800_

12. 2 × 60 = _120_

13. 5 × 40 = _200_

14. 6 × 8000 = _48,000_

15. 4 × 200 = _800_

16. 3 × 8000 = _24,000_

17. 7 × 900 = _6300_

18. 8 × 300 = _2400_

Problem Solving

19. Runners in the Tri-City Marathon drank 2000 cases of water. There were 6 bottles of water in each case. How many bottles of water did the runners drink in all? _6 × 2000 = 12,000; 12,000 bottles_

Estimate Products

Name _____

Date _____

Rounding:

Round the greater factor to its greatest place value. Then multiply.

$$\begin{array}{r} \$2.76 \longrightarrow \$3.00 \\ \times \quad 3 \qquad \times \quad 3 \\ \hline \text{about } \$9.00 \end{array}$$

Front–End Estimation:

Use the value of the front digit of the greater factor. Then multiply.

$$\begin{array}{r} \$2.76 \longrightarrow \$2.00 \\ \times \quad 3 \qquad \times \quad 3 \\ \hline \text{about } \$6.00 \end{array}$$

Multiply mentally. Look for a pattern.

1. $3 \times 200 =$ _600_   **2.** $3 \times 300 =$ _900_   **3.** $3 \times 400 =$ _1200_

4. $3 \times 500 =$ _1500_   **5.** $3 \times 600 =$ _1800_   **6.** $3 \times 700 =$ _2100_

Estimate by rounding.

7.
$$\begin{array}{r} 23 \\ \times \quad 3 \\ \hline 60 \end{array}$$

8.
$$\begin{array}{r} 44 \\ \times \quad 5 \\ \hline 200 \end{array}$$

9.
$$\begin{array}{r} 36 \\ \times \quad 2 \\ \hline 80 \end{array}$$

10.
$$\begin{array}{r} \$.78 \\ \times \quad 7 \\ \hline \$5.60 \end{array}$$

11.
$$\begin{array}{r} 16¢ \\ \times \quad 4 \\ \hline 80¢ \end{array}$$

12.
$$\begin{array}{r} \$.66 \\ \times \quad 6 \\ \hline \$4.20 \end{array}$$

13.
$$\begin{array}{r} 453 \\ \times \quad 3 \\ \hline 2000 \end{array}$$

14.
$$\begin{array}{r} 269 \\ \times \quad 3 \\ \hline 900 \end{array}$$

15.
$$\begin{array}{r} \$6.71 \\ \times \quad 5 \\ \hline \$35.00 \end{array}$$

16.
$$\begin{array}{r} \$3.93 \\ \times \quad 2 \\ \hline \$8.00 \end{array}$$

17.
$$\begin{array}{r} \$5.27 \\ \times \quad 6 \\ \hline \$30.00 \end{array}$$

18.
$$\begin{array}{r} \$1.81 \\ \times \quad 2 \\ \hline \$4.00 \end{array}$$

Estimate. First round, then use front-end estimation.

19.
$$\begin{array}{r} 351 \\ \times \quad 3 \\ \hline 1200; 900 \end{array}$$

20.
$$\begin{array}{r} 557 \\ \times \quad 4 \\ \hline 2400; 2000 \end{array}$$

21.
$$\begin{array}{r} 479 \\ \times \quad 5 \\ \hline 2500; 2000 \end{array}$$

22.
$$\begin{array}{r} \$5.33 \\ \times \quad 2 \\ \hline \$10; \$10 \end{array}$$

23.
$$\begin{array}{r} \$4.84 \\ \times \quad 3 \\ \hline \$15; \$12 \end{array}$$

24.
$$\begin{array}{r} \$6.58 \\ \times \quad 6 \\ \hline \$42; \$36 \end{array}$$

25. $\$4.82 \times 2 =$ _$10, $8_   **26.** $648 \times 3 =$ _1800,1800_   **27.** $\$7.36 \times 4 =$ _$28, $28_

Problem Solving

28. Brigitta bought 3 pairs of socks. Each pair cost $2.29. **About** how much money did she spend?

$3 \times \$2.00 = \$6.00$; about $6.00

29. Justin bought 2 tee-shirts. Each shirt cost $8.69. **About** how much did he spend?

$2 \times \$9.00 = \$18.00$; about $18.00

Multiply Two Digits

Name _____

Date _____

$14 \times 2 = \underline{?}$

Estimate:

$14 \longrightarrow 10$

$\times\ 2 \longrightarrow \times\ 2$

about 20

Multiply:

tens	ones
1	4
×	2
	8

tens	ones
1	4
×	2
2	8

Multiply.

1. 41
    × 2
    ——
    82

2. 12
    × 3
    ——
    36

3. 23
    × 3
    ——
    69

4. 33
    × 2
    ——
    66

5. 42
    × 2
    ——
    84

6. 11
    × 6
    ——
    66

7. 20
    × 4
    ——
    80

8. 21
    × 4
    ——
    84

9. 30
    × 2
    ——
    60

10. 32
    × 3
    ——
    96

11. 11
    × 3
    ——
    33

12. 12
    × 4
    ——
    48

13. 31
    × 3
    ——
    93

14. 32
    × 2
    ——
    64

15. 43
    × 2
    ——
    86

Align. Then find the product.

16. 2 × 14
    14
    × 2
    ——
    28

17. 2 × 22
    22
    × 2
    ——
    44

18. 2 × 31
    31
    × 2
    ——
    62

19. 3 × 12
    12
    × 3
    ——
    36

20. 3 × 21
    21
    × 3
    ——
    63

21. 3 × 22
    22
    × 3
    ——
    66

22. 2 × 42
    42
    × 2
    ——
    84

23. 4 × 22
    22
    × 4
    ——
    88

24. 3 × 33
    33
    × 3
    ——
    99

Problem Solving

25. Manuel ordered furniture for a new office building. He ordered 2 chairs for each of 43 offices. How many chairs did he order? _____ $2 \times 43 = 86$; 86 chairs

26. A blacksmith made 4 shoes for each of 21 horses. How many horseshoes did he make? _____ $4 \times 21 = 84$; 84 horseshoes

Multiply with Models

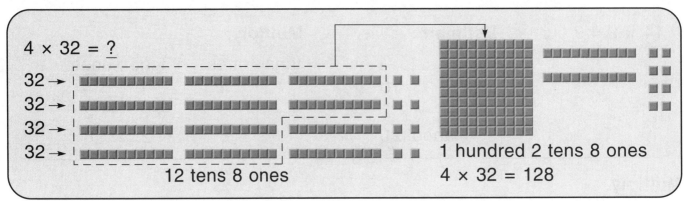

$4 \times 32 = \underline{?}$

$32 \rightarrow$

$32 \rightarrow$

$32 \rightarrow$

$32 \rightarrow$

12 tens 8 ones

1 hundred 2 tens 8 ones

$4 \times 32 = 128$

Complete. You may use models.

1. $3 \times 4 = \underline{\quad 12 \quad}$ **2.** $6 \times 5 = \underline{\quad 30 \quad}$ **3.** $2 \times 9 = \underline{\quad 18 \quad}$

$3 \times 40 = \underline{\quad 120 \quad}$ $6 \times 50 = \underline{\quad 300 \quad}$ $2 \times 90 = \underline{\quad 180 \quad}$

Match the multiplication sentence with the model.

4. $5 \times 12 = 60 \underline{\quad b \quad}$

a.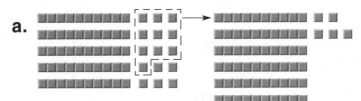

5. $5 \times 13 = 65 \underline{\quad a \quad}$

b.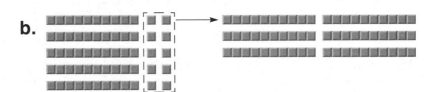

6. $3 \times 15 = 45 \underline{\quad d \quad}$

c.

7. $6 \times 12 = 72 \underline{\quad c \quad}$

d.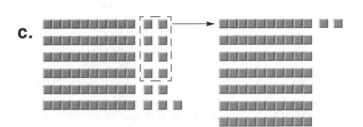

Multiply with Regrouping

Name _____

Date _____

$6 \times 13 = \underline{?}$

First estimate:
$6 \times 10 = 60$
Then multiply.

Multiply the ones. Regroup.	Multiply the tens. Then add.
$\overset{1}{1}3$ $\times\ \ 6$ $\overline{\quad 8}$	$\overset{1}{1}3$ $\times\ \ 6$ $\overline{78}$

Use rounding to estimate the product. Then multiply.

1. 45   2. 49   3. 26   4. 18   5. 15

1. 45 $\times\ \ 2$ $\overline{90}$	2. 49 $\times\ \ 2$ $\overline{98}$	3. 26 $\times\ \ 3$ $\overline{78}$	4. 18 $\times\ \ 2$ $\overline{36}$	5. 15 $\times\ \ 6$ $\overline{90}$
6. 19¢ $\times\ \ 4$ $\overline{76¢}$	7. $24 $\times\ \ 3$ $\overline{\$72}$	8. 48¢ $\times\ \ 2$ $\overline{96¢}$	9. 25¢ $\times\ \ 3$ $\overline{75¢}$	10. $47 $\times\ \ 2$ $\overline{\$94}$
11. 24 $\times\ \ 4$ $\overline{96}$	12. 18 $\times\ \ 5$ $\overline{90}$	13. 27 $\times\ \ 3$ $\overline{81}$	14. 13 $\times\ \ 4$ $\overline{52}$	15. 37 $\times\ \ 2$ $\overline{74}$
16. $35 $\times\ \ 2$ $\overline{\$70}$	17. $23 $\times\ \ 4$ $\overline{\$92}$	18. $39 $\times\ \ 2$ $\overline{\$78}$	19. 29¢ $\times\ \ 3$ $\overline{87¢}$	20. 12¢ $\times\ \ 8$ $\overline{96¢}$

Find the product.

21. 2×16 16 $\times\ \ 2$ $\overline{32}$	**22.** 2×26 26 $\times\ \ 2$ $\overline{52}$	**23.** 2×38 38 $\times\ \ 2$ $\overline{76}$
24. $3 \times \$15$ $15 $\times\ \ 3$ $\overline{\$45}$	**25.** $3 \times 26¢$ 26¢ $\times\ \ 3$ $\overline{78¢}$	**26.** $3 \times \$28$ $28 $\times\ \ 3$ $\overline{\$84}$

Problem Solving

27. Two buses went to the park. Each bus carried 25 passengers. How many passengers were there in all?

$\underline{2 \times 25 = 50;\ 50\ passengers}$

More Multiplying with Regrouping

Name _____

Date _____

$4 \times 54 = \underline{?}$

First estimate:
$4 \times 50 = 200$
Then multiply.

Multiply the ones. Regroup.	Multiply the tens. Then add.
$\begin{array}{r} \overset{1}{5}4 \\ \times\ 4 \\ \hline 6 \end{array}$	$\begin{array}{r} \overset{1}{5}4 \\ \times\ 4 \\ \hline 216 \end{array}$

Use rounding to estimate the product. Then multiply.

1. $\begin{array}{r} 30 \\ \times\ 4 \\ \hline 120 \end{array}$
2. $\begin{array}{r} 31 \\ \times\ 8 \\ \hline 248 \end{array}$
3. $\begin{array}{r} 60 \\ \times\ 7 \\ \hline 420 \end{array}$
4. $\begin{array}{r} 52 \\ \times\ 3 \\ \hline 156 \end{array}$
5. $\begin{array}{r} 41 \\ \times\ 9 \\ \hline 369 \end{array}$

6. $\begin{array}{r} 38 \\ \times\ 3 \\ \hline 114 \end{array}$
7. $\begin{array}{r} 17 \\ \times\ 6 \\ \hline 102 \end{array}$
8. $\begin{array}{r} 29 \\ \times\ 5 \\ \hline 145 \end{array}$
9. $\begin{array}{r} 16 \\ \times\ 7 \\ \hline 112 \end{array}$
10. $\begin{array}{r} 43 \\ \times\ 4 \\ \hline 172 \end{array}$

11. $\begin{array}{r} 26 \\ \times\ 5 \\ \hline 130 \end{array}$
12. $\begin{array}{r} 63 \\ \times\ 4 \\ \hline 252 \end{array}$
13. $\begin{array}{r} 47 \\ \times\ 3 \\ \hline 141 \end{array}$
14. $\begin{array}{r} 32 \\ \times\ 6 \\ \hline 192 \end{array}$
15. $\begin{array}{r} 53 \\ \times\ 5 \\ \hline 265 \end{array}$

16. $\begin{array}{r} 38 \\ \times\ 4 \\ \hline 152 \end{array}$
17. $\begin{array}{r} 27 \\ \times\ 6 \\ \hline 162 \end{array}$
18. $\begin{array}{r} 83 \\ \times\ 4 \\ \hline 332 \end{array}$
19. $\begin{array}{r} 65 \\ \times\ 4 \\ \hline 260 \end{array}$
20. $\begin{array}{r} 78 \\ \times\ 2 \\ \hline 156 \end{array}$

Find the product.

21. 3×66 $\quad \begin{array}{r} 66 \\ \times\ 3 \\ \hline 198 \end{array}$
22. 8×27 $\quad \begin{array}{r} 27 \\ \times\ 8 \\ \hline 216 \end{array}$
23. 9×34 $\quad \begin{array}{r} 34 \\ \times\ 9 \\ \hline 306 \end{array}$

24. 5×18 $\quad \begin{array}{r} 18 \\ \times\ 5 \\ \hline 90 \end{array}$
25. 6×19 $\quad \begin{array}{r} 19 \\ \times\ 6 \\ \hline 114 \end{array}$
26. 8×32 $\quad \begin{array}{r} 32 \\ \times\ 8 \\ \hline 256 \end{array}$

Problem Solving

27. Suzanne fed birds outside her window.
    She used 4 bags of birdseed each week.
    How many bags did she use in one year? $\underline{\quad 4 \times 52 = 208;\ 208\ \text{bags} \quad}$

Multiply Three Digits

Name _____

Date _____

Multiply: 3 × 213
First estimate: 3 × 200 = 600

Multiply the ones.	Multiply the tens.	Multiply the hundreds.
213	213	213
× 3	× 3	× 3
9	39	639

Use rounding to estimate. Then multiply.

1. 231
× 3
693

2. 331
× 2
662

3. 212
× 4
848

4. 112
× 4
448

5. 113
× 3
339

6. 202
× 3
606

7. 101
× 8
808

8. 324
× 2
648

9. 222
× 2
444

10. 133
× 3
399

11. 111
× 7
777

12. 402
× 2
804

13. 200
× 2
400

14. 101
× 9
909

15. 413
× 2
826

Multiply.

16. 2321
× 3
6963

17. 4134
× 2
8268

18. 2212
× 4
8848

19. 4334
× 2
8668

20. 1323
× 3
3969

Problem Solving

21. Ms. Diaz ordered supplies for the Lakeview School. She ordered 4 boxes of pencils. Each box held 120 pencils. How many pencils did she order?

4 × 120 = 480; 480 pencils

22. Ms. Diaz ordered craft sticks. She ordered 320 craft sticks for each of 2 classrooms. How many craft sticks did she order altogether?

2 × 320 = 640; 640 sticks

131

Regroup in Multiplication

Name _____

Date _____

Multiply: 5×135

First estimate: $5 \times 100 = 500$

Multiply the ones. Regroup.	Multiply the tens. Add. Regroup again.	Multiply the hundreds. Add.

$$\begin{array}{r} \overset{2}{1}35 \\ \times\ \ 5 \\ \hline 5 \end{array}$$

$$\begin{array}{r} \overset{1}{1}\overset{2}{3}5 \\ \times\ \ 5 \\ \hline 75 \end{array}$$

$$\begin{array}{r} \overset{1}{1}\overset{2}{3}5 \\ \times\ \ 5 \\ \hline 675 \end{array}$$

Use rounding to estimate the product. Then multiply.

1. $\begin{array}{r} 238 \\ \times\ \ 3 \\ \hline 714 \end{array}$

2. $\begin{array}{r} 153 \\ \times\ \ 4 \\ \hline 612 \end{array}$

3. $\begin{array}{r} 275 \\ \times\ \ 3 \\ \hline 825 \end{array}$

4. $\begin{array}{r} 167 \\ \times\ \ 5 \\ \hline 835 \end{array}$

5. $\begin{array}{r} 389 \\ \times\ \ 2 \\ \hline 778 \end{array}$

6. $\begin{array}{r} 195 \\ \times\ \ 5 \\ \hline 975 \end{array}$

7. $\begin{array}{r} 169 \\ \times\ \ 4 \\ \hline 676 \end{array}$

8. $\begin{array}{r} 157 \\ \times\ \ 6 \\ \hline 942 \end{array}$

9. $\begin{array}{r} 248 \\ \times\ \ 3 \\ \hline 744 \end{array}$

10. $\begin{array}{r} 134 \\ \times\ \ 7 \\ \hline 938 \end{array}$

11. $\begin{array}{r} 258 \\ \times\ \ 3 \\ \hline 774 \end{array}$

12. $\begin{array}{r} 248 \\ \times\ \ 4 \\ \hline 992 \end{array}$

13. $\begin{array}{r} 146 \\ \times\ \ 6 \\ \hline 876 \end{array}$

14. $\begin{array}{r} 128 \\ \times\ \ 7 \\ \hline 896 \end{array}$

15. $\begin{array}{r} 163 \\ \times\ \ 5 \\ \hline 815 \end{array}$

Find the product.

16. $\begin{array}{r} 2273 \\ \times\ \ \ \ 3 \\ \hline 6819 \end{array}$

17. $\begin{array}{r} 3342 \\ \times\ \ \ \ 2 \\ \hline 6684 \end{array}$

18. $\begin{array}{r} 2128 \\ \times\ \ \ \ 4 \\ \hline 8512 \end{array}$

19. $\begin{array}{r} 3193 \\ \times\ \ \ \ 3 \\ \hline 9579 \end{array}$

20. $\begin{array}{r} 2318 \\ \times\ \ \ \ 2 \\ \hline 4636 \end{array}$

21. $\begin{array}{r} 1161 \\ \times\ \ \ \ 5 \\ \hline 5805 \end{array}$

22. $\begin{array}{r} 2163 \\ \times\ \ \ \ 4 \\ \hline 8652 \end{array}$

23. $\begin{array}{r} 3217 \\ \times\ \ \ \ 3 \\ \hline 9651 \end{array}$

24. $\begin{array}{r} 1191 \\ \times\ \ \ \ 6 \\ \hline 7146 \end{array}$

25. $\begin{array}{r} 1102 \\ \times\ \ \ \ 7 \\ \hline 7714 \end{array}$

Problem Solving

26. Marcel goes to a college that is 258 miles from home. When he drives home for a weekend and then returns, how many miles does he drive?

_____ 2×258 mi; 516 mi

Regroup Twice in Multiplication

Name _____

Date _____

Multiply: 6 × 1153
First estimate: 6 × 1000 = 6000

Multiply the ones. Regroup.	Multiply the tens. Add. Regroup again.	Multiply the hundreds. Add.	Multiply the thousands.
$\overset{1}{}$ $\$11\overset{1}{5}3$ × 6 8	$\overset{3\,1}{}$ $\$1153$ × 6 18	$\overset{3\,1}{}$ $\$1153$ × 6 918	$\overset{3\,1}{}$ $\$1153$ × 6 6918

Round to estimate the product. Then multiply.

1. 158
× 2
316

2. 187
× 3
561

3. 177
× 5
885

4. $127
× 6
$762

5. $148
× 3
$444

6. 1294
× 7
9058

7. 2355
× 2
4710

8. 2264
× 3
6792

9. 2245
× 3
6735

10. 2275
× 4
9100

11. $3389
× 2
$6778

12. $2164
× 3
$6492

13. $1135
× 8
$9080

14. $3179
× 2
$6358

15. $2164
× 4
$8656

Find the product.

16. $258
× 2
$516

17. 197
× 3
591

18. 1254
× 3
3762

19. $1269
× 2
$2538

20. 136
× 7
952

21. 137
× 6
822

22. $1138
× 6
$6828

23. 2239
× 4
8956

24. 1129
× 7
7903

25. 2228
× 4
8912

Problem Solving

26. The monthly rent for Brandon's family's apartment is $2055. How much rent does Brandon pay over three months?

$2055 × 3 = $6165; $6165

Problem Solving Strategy: Work Backward

Name _____

Date _____

Alice gave Tim 25 empty bottles for the recycling bin. Then Tim broke 7 bottles. He now has 32 bottles. How many bottles did Tim have to begin with?

To find out how many bottles Tim had at the beginning, start at the end and work backwards.

$$32 \;-\; 25 \;+\; 7 \;=\; \underline{?}$$

bottles left	bottles from Alice	bottles broke	bottles at the beginning

$32 - 25 + 7 = 14$

Tim had 14 bottles to begin with.

Work backward to solve. Do your work on a separate sheet of paper.

1. Bart's brother got paid every week. He always kept $85 for groceries and $35 for lunch and bus fare. He had $140 left. How much money did he get paid every week?

$140 + $35 + $85 = $250; $250

2. Yvonne's doctor tells her not to eat for 14 hours before her appointment at 10 A.M. on Tuesday. When is the last time Yvonne can eat before her appointment?

8 P.M. on Monday

3. Kyle found 3 baseball cards in his room. His sister gave him 2 more cards. He then had a total of 11 baseball cards. How many cards did Kyle start with?

$11 - 2 - 3 = 6$; 6 cards

4. Monica wants to take the 9:25 A.M. train to Philadelphia. The trip from her house to the train station takes 45 minutes. By what time must Monica leave her house?

8:40 A.M.

5. For Donovan's birthday last week, his sister and brother each gave him 2 games. Then he bought 3 games with his birthday money. Now he has 15 games. How many games did he have to begin with?

$15 - 3 - 2 - 2 = 8$; 8 games

6. Eugene got home at 4:15 P.M. He had walked for 30 minutes from Joe's house, where the two boys spent 1 hour and 15 minutes doing homework. At what time did Eugene and Joe start their homework?

2:30 P.M.

Problem-Solving Applications: Mixed Review

Name _____

Date _____

Solve each problem and explain the method you used. If needed, do all your work on a separate sheet of paper.

> Read > Plan > Solve > Check

Strategy File

Use These Strategies
Guess and Test
Logical Reasoning
Work Backward
Use More Than One Step
Choose the Operation

1. In a basketball game, Mike made 15 3-point baskets. How many points did Mike score in that game?

$15 \times 3 = 45$; 45 points

2. Jin and Rhonda together spent $97 on sports equipment. If Rhonda spent $7 more than Jin, how much did Jin spend?

$45 + $52 = $97;
$52 − $45 = $7; Jin spent $45

3. Lindsay bought 8 steaks at the grocery store. Each steak cost $5.27. About how much money did Lindsay spend for the steaks?

$8 \times $5.27 \rightarrow 8 \times $5.00 = $40;
about $40.00

4. John earns $7.15 for each lawn he mows. How much will John make for mowing 6 lawns?

$7.15 \times 6 = $42.90; $42.90

5. Lara cut a piece of rope into 13 equal pieces. If each piece is 4 feet long, how long was the rope before it was cut?

$13 \times 4 = 52$; 52 feet long

6. Erin made a necklace with 9 black beads, twice as many purple beads as black beads and 6 more gray beads than purple beads. How many beads are on the necklace in all?

$9 \times 2 = 18$; $18 + 6 = 24$;
$9 + 18 + 24 = 51$; 51 beads

7. There are 27 bikes on the bike rack. It has 4 green bikes, 8 black bikes, 2 purple bikes, 7 silver bikes, and the rest of the bikes are orange. How many bikes are orange?

$4 + 8 + 2 + 7 = 21$; $27 − 21 = 6$;
6 bikes are orange

8. Dinner for four friends totaled $46. Sean's meal was $12, Jeanine's meal was $11, and Becca's meal was $8. Whose meal was the least expensive?

$12 + $11 + $8 = $31; $46 −
$31 = $15; $8 < $11 < $12 < $15;
Becca's meal

9. Bob bought an 18-pack of gum. He gave 4 pieces to Erica and 5 pieces to his mother. His brother then gave him a pack with 10 pieces in it. How many pieces of gum does Bob have now?

$18 − 4 − 5 = 9$; $9 + 10 = 19$;
19 pieces of gum

Use with Lesson 10-11, text pages 356–357.   Copyright © William H. Sadlier, Inc. All rights reserved.   135

Division Sense

Name _____

Date _____

Estimate: 29 ÷ 4	Estimate: 71 ÷ 2
6 × 4 = 24 ← too small	2 tens × 2 = 4 tens ← too small
7 × 4 = 28 ←	3 tens × 2 = 6 tens ←
29 is between 24 and 32.	**7 tens is between 4 tens and 8 tens.**
8 × 4 = 32 ← too large	4 tens × 2 = 8 tens ← too large
Try **7**.	Try **3**. Write zeros for the other digits.
So 29 ÷ 4 is about **7**.	So 71 ÷ 2 is about **30**.

Use facts to estimate.

1. 45 ÷ 6 = __7__ **2.** 64 ÷ 9 = __7__ **3.** 25 ÷ 3 = __8__ **4.** 37 ÷ 5 = __7__

5. 17 ÷ 2 = __8__ **6.** 19 ÷ 3 = __6__ **7.** 58 ÷ 8 = __7__ **8.** 37 ÷ 7 = __5__

9. 6)2̄6̄ → 4 **10.** 4)3̄0̄ → 7 **11.** 5)4̄2̄ → 8 **12.** 3)2̄3̄ → 7 **13.** 9)3̄1̄ → 3 **14.** 7)4̄5̄ → 6

Use tens to estimate.

15. 41 ÷ 2 = __20__ **16.** 64 ÷ 5 = __10__ **17.** 97 ÷ 4 = __20__ **18.** 58 ÷ 3 = __20__

19. 92 ÷ 7 = __10__ **20.** 84 ÷ 6 = __10__ **21.** 75 ÷ 2 = __30__ **22.** 88 ÷ 3 = __30__

23. 4)8̄7̄ → 20 **24.** 3)5̄6̄ → 20 **25.** 2)8̄3̄ → 40 **26.** 6)9̄9̄ → 10 **27.** 5)8̄6̄ → 10 **28.** 3)9̄4̄ → 30

Divide mentally.

29.　　6 ÷ 2 = __3__　　　　**30.**　　7 ÷ 7 = __1__　　　　**31.**　　10 ÷ 5 = __2__

　　　　60 ÷ 2 = __30__　　　　　　70 ÷ 7 = __10__　　　　　　100 ÷ 5 = __20__

　　　600 ÷ 2 = __300__　　　　　700 ÷ 7 = __100__　　　　1000 ÷ 5 = __200__

Problem Solving

32. There are 88 stickers. **About** how many stickers can 3 friends share equally?

__88 ÷ 3; about 20 stickers__

Division with Remainders

Name _____

Date _____

10 ÷ 4 = 2
remainder 2   or 2 R2

10 ÷ 3 = 3
remainder 1   or 3 R1

13 ÷ 5 = 2
remainder 3   or 2 R3

Complete.

1. ⊙⊙ ●

3 ÷ 2 = ___1___

remainder ___1___

2. ⊙⊙⊙ ⊙⊙⊙ ●●

8 ÷ 3 = ___2___

remainder ___2___

3. ⊙⊙⊙⊙⊙ ⊙⊙⊙⊙⊙ ● ⊙⊙⊙⊙⊙

16 ÷ 5 = ___3___

remainder ___1___

4. ⊙⊙⊙⊙⊙ ●●●● ⊙⊙⊙⊙⊙

14 ÷ 5 = ___2___

remainder ___4___

5. ⊙⊙⊙⊙⊙ ●

11 ÷ 2 = ___5___

remainder ___1___

6. ⊙⊙⊙⊙⊙ ●● ⊙⊙⊙⊙⊙ ⊙⊙⊙⊙⊙

17 ÷ 5 = ___3___

remainder ___2___

Ring circles to show each division. Find the quotient and remainder.

Circles may vary.

7. 14 ÷ 6 = ___2___

remainder ___2___

8. 14 ÷ 3 = ___4___

remainder ___2___

9. 19 ÷ 5 = ___3___

remainder ___4___

Find the quotient and remainder.

10. 9 ÷ 6 = ___1 R3___

11. 15 ÷ 2 = ___7 R1___

12. 19 ÷ 4 = ___4 R3___

13. 19 ÷ 6 = ___3 R1___

14. 15 ÷ 4 = ___3 R3___

15. 28 ÷ 9 = ___3 R1___

One-Digit Quotients

Name _____

Date _____

Divide: $16 \div 3 = $? or $3\overline{)16}$?

Think:

$4 \times 3 = 12$ [too small]

$5 \times 3 = 15$ Try **5.**

$6 \times 3 = 18$ [too large]

$$\begin{array}{r} 5 \\ 3\overline{)16} \end{array} \qquad \begin{array}{r} 5 \\ 3\overline{)16} \\ 15 \end{array} \qquad \begin{array}{r} 5 \\ 3\overline{)16} \\ -15 \\ \hline 1 \end{array} \qquad \begin{array}{r} 5 \text{ R1} \\ 3\overline{)16} \\ -15 \\ \hline 1 \end{array}$$

Estimate. About how many:

1. 5s in 11? **2.** 5s in 19? **3.** 2s in 15? **4.** 3s in 29? **5.** 4s in 31?

    2   3   7   9   7

Find the quotient and remainder.

6. $\begin{array}{r} 6 \text{ R1} \\ 3\overline{)19} \\ -18 \\ \hline 1 \end{array}$
7. $\begin{array}{r} 6 \text{ R3} \\ 4\overline{)27} \\ -24 \\ \hline 3 \end{array}$
8. $\begin{array}{r} 8 \text{ R1} \\ 2\overline{)17} \\ -16 \\ \hline 1 \end{array}$
9. $\begin{array}{r} 6 \text{ R2} \\ 3\overline{)20} \\ -18 \\ \hline 2 \end{array}$
10. $\begin{array}{r} 4 \text{ R1} \\ 6\overline{)25} \\ -24 \\ \hline 1 \end{array}$

11. $\begin{array}{r} 5 \text{ R4} \\ 7\overline{)39} \\ -35 \\ \hline 4 \end{array}$
12. $\begin{array}{r} 2 \text{ R2} \\ 9\overline{)20} \\ -18 \\ \hline 2 \end{array}$
13. $\begin{array}{r} 3 \text{ R3} \\ 8\overline{)27} \\ -24 \\ \hline 3 \end{array}$
14. $\begin{array}{r} 6 \text{ R3} \\ 6\overline{)39} \\ -36 \\ \hline 3 \end{array}$
15. $\begin{array}{r} 7 \text{ R1} \\ 7\overline{)50} \\ -49 \\ \hline 1 \end{array}$

Divide and check.

16. $47 \div 6$ ___7 R5___

17. $18 \div 7$ ___2 R4___

18. $57 \div 6$ ___9 R3___

19. $66 \div 7$ ___9 R3___

20. $37 \div 8$ ___4 R5___

21. $45 \div 8$ ___5 R5___

Problem Solving

22. A snack tray held 13 bags of popcorn. After 5 people bought the same number bags each, there were 3 bags left. How many bags of popcorn did each person buy?

$13 \div 5 = 2 \text{ R3}$; 2 bags

Two-Digit Quotients

Name _____

Date _____

Divide.	Multiply.	Subtract and compare.	Bring down the ones. Divide the ones.
$\dfrac{1}{4)\overline{68}}$	$\times$ ↱1 4)$\overline{68}$ ↳4	1 4)$\overline{68}$ −4 ──── 2	17 4)$\overline{68}$ −4↓ ──── 28 −28 ──── No remainder → 0

Divide and check.

1.
```
  28
4)96
 -8
 ──
 16
-16
 ──
  0
```

2.
```
  28
3)84
 -6
 ──
 24
-24
 ──
  0
```

3.
```
  29
2)58
 -4
 ──
 18
-18
 ──
  0
```

4.
```
  18
4)72
 -4
 ──
 32
-32
 ──
  0
```

5.
```
  19
3)57
 -3
 ──
 27
-27
 ──
  0
```

6.
```
  19
5)95
 -5
 ──
 45
-45
 ──
  0
```

7.
```
  13
4)52
 -4
 ──
 12
-12
 ──
  0
```

8.
```
  27
3)81
 -6
 ──
 21
-21
 ──
  0
```

9.
```
  49
2)98
 -8
 ──
 18
-18
 ──
  0
```

10.
```
  15
5)75
 -5
 ──
 25
-25
 ──
  0
```

11.
```
   62
3)186
 -18
 ───
   6
  -6
  ──
   0
```

12.
```
   89
2)178
 -16
 ───
  18
 -18
 ───
   0
```

13.
```
   57
3)171
 -15
 ───
  21
 -21
 ───
   0
```

14.
```
   37
4)148
 -12
 ───
  28
 -28
 ───
   0
```

15.
```
   71
5)355
 -35
 ───
   5
  -5
  ──
   0
```

Problem Solving

16. Hari has 184 glass turtles. If he puts the same number on each of 4 shelves, how many turtles are on each shelf?

$\underline{\quad 184 \div 4 = 46;\ 46 \text{ turtles} \quad}$

17. Katy's 56 banners cover her 4 walls. Each wall has the same number of banners. At most, how many banners are on each wall?

$\underline{\quad 56 \div 4 = 14;\ 14 \text{ banners} \quad}$

Quotients with Remainders

Name _____

Date _____

$85 \div 6 = \underline{?}$

$$\begin{array}{r} \times \\ \overset{\displaystyle 1}{6)\overline{85}} \\ 6 \end{array}$$

$$\begin{array}{r} 1 \\ 6)\overline{85} \\ -6 \\ \hline 2 \end{array}$$

$$\begin{array}{r} 14 \\ 6)\overline{85} \\ -6\downarrow \\ \hline 25 \\ -24 \end{array}$$

$$\begin{array}{r} 14\ R1 \\ 6)\overline{85} \\ -6 \\ \hline 25 \\ -24 \\ \hline 1 \end{array}$$

Check:

$$\begin{array}{r} 2 \\ 14 \\ \times\ 6 \\ \hline 84 \\ +\ 1 \\ \hline 85 \end{array}$$

Divide and check.

1. $\begin{array}{r} 17\ R1 \\ 3)\overline{52} \\ -3 \\ \hline 22 \\ -21 \\ \hline 1 \end{array}$

2. $\begin{array}{r} 12\ R1 \\ 4)\overline{49} \\ -4 \\ \hline 9 \\ -8 \\ \hline 1 \end{array}$

3. $\begin{array}{r} 16\ R3 \\ 4)\overline{67} \\ -4 \\ \hline 27 \\ -24 \\ \hline 3 \end{array}$

4. $\begin{array}{r} 19\ R2 \\ 5)\overline{97} \\ -5 \\ \hline 47 \\ -45 \\ \hline 2 \end{array}$

5. $\begin{array}{r} 13\ R4 \\ 6)\overline{82} \\ -6 \\ \hline 22 \\ -18 \\ \hline 4 \end{array}$

6. $\begin{array}{r} 11\ R1 \\ 8)\overline{89} \\ -8 \\ \hline 9 \\ -8 \\ \hline 1 \end{array}$

7. $\begin{array}{r} 17\ R2 \\ 5)\overline{87} \\ -5 \\ \hline 37 \\ -35 \\ \hline 2 \end{array}$

8. $\begin{array}{r} 11\ R2 \\ 7)\overline{79} \\ -7 \\ \hline 9 \\ -7 \\ \hline 2 \end{array}$

9. $\begin{array}{r} 16\ R2 \\ 6)\overline{98} \\ -6 \\ \hline 38 \\ -36 \\ \hline 2 \end{array}$

10. $\begin{array}{r} 12\ R3 \\ 8)\overline{99} \\ -8 \\ \hline 19 \\ -16 \\ \hline 3 \end{array}$

Find the quotient and remainder.

11. $98 \div 8$ __12 R2__

12. $65 \div 4$ __16 R1__

13. $59 \div 5$ __11 R4__

14. $89 \div 3$ __29 R2__

15. $49 \div 4$ __12 R1__

16. $74 \div 6$ __12 R2__

Problem Solving

17. Inez has 94 stamps in her collection. She put the same number of stamps into 8 envelopes. At most, how many stamps could be in each envelope? How many would be left over?

$94 \div 8 = 11\ R6$; 11 stamps in each envelope; 6 left over

Estimate Quotients

Name _____

Date _____

Estimate.

$5.86 ÷ 3 = __?__

$5.86 rounds to $6

$6 ÷ 3 = $2

$5.86 ÷ 3 is about $2.

$15.37 ÷ 5 = __?__

$15.37 rounds to $15

$15 ÷ 5 = $3

$15.37 ÷ 5 is about $3.

75 ÷ 4 = __?__

75 rounds to 80

80 ÷ 4 = 20

75 ÷ 4 is about 20.

Round to the nearest ten or dollar.

1. 68 __70__   **2.** 42 __40__   **3.** 85 __90__   **4.** 17 __20__

5. $1.16 __$1__   **6.** $3.08 __$3__   **7.** $24.92 __$25__   **8.** $17.25 __$17__

Estimate the quotient.

9. $\overset{30}{2\overline{)62}}$ **10.** $\overset{10}{4\overline{)38}}$ **11.** $\overset{\$3}{3\overline{)\$8.90}}$ **12.** $\overset{\$1}{6\overline{)\$5.95}}$

13. $\overset{\$7}{3\overline{)\$20.99}}$ **14.** $\overset{\$6}{6\overline{)\$35.89}}$ **15.** $\overset{\$3}{5\overline{)\$14.75}}$ **16.** $\overset{\$8}{8\overline{)\$64.25}}$

17. $\overset{\$8}{8\overline{)\$63.68}}$ **18.** $\overset{\$9}{5\overline{)\$44.79}}$ **19.** $\overset{\$4}{6\overline{)\$24.16}}$ **20.** $\overset{\$5}{7\overline{)\$35.40}}$

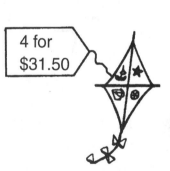

4 for $27.75

3 for $27.30

4 for $31.50

2 for $19.55

5 for $24.50

Use the art above to estimate each answer.

21. About how much does 1 tee shirt cost? $28 ÷ 4 = $7; about $7

22. About how much does 1 belt cost? $20 ÷ 2 = $10; about $10

23. About how much does 1 pair of shorts cost? $27 ÷ 3 = $9; about $9

24. How many kites can be bought for $23? $32 ÷ 4 = 8; $24 ÷ 8 = 3; about 3

25. How many toy trucks can be bought for $9? $25 ÷ 5 = $5; $10 ÷ 5 = 2; about 2

               141

Problem-Solving Strategy: Interpret the Remainder

Name _____

Date _____

> There were 19 people camping at the park. Each cabin sleeps 4 people. How many cabins were needed for all 19 people?
>
> **Think:** What is 19 divided by 4?
>
> $$4)\overline{19}^{\,4R3}$$
>
> There were 4 full cabins and 3 people in another cabin. So 5 cabins were needed.

Solve. Do your work on a separate sheet of paper.

1. Lydia's Nursery delivered 65 tree seedlings to the park grounds crew. They planted 9 seedlings at each campsite. How many campsites are there? How many seedlings were left?

   $65 \div 9 = 7$ campsites; 2 left

2. Eric spotted 58 geese flying north. They were in 3 groups. Two groups had an equal number of geese and the third group had one more than that. How many geese were in each group?

   $58 \div 3 = 19R1$; 19, 19, 20

3. Isaac wants to clear 50 feet of new trail in 6 days. If he clears about the same number of feet each day, how many feet of trail will he need to clear each day?

   $50 \div 6 = 8R2$; 9 feet

4. There were 37 people who came to the Jones family picnic. Five people came in each car, except for the last car, which held 2 people. How many cars did they use?

   $37 \div 5 = 7R2$; 8 cars

5. A visitor bought 6 park maps. She gave the clerk $50 and received $2 change. How much did each map cost?

   $\$50 \div 6 = \$8 \ R\$2$; $8 each

6. A group of 8 campers has 30 marshmallows to share for toasting. Can each camper toast 4 marshmallows?

   $30 \div 8 = 3R6$; No

7. The road through the park is 23 miles long. Information signs are placed every 5 miles. How many signs are along the road?

   $23 \div 5 = 4R3$; 4 signs

8. Dana has $9. She spent an equal amount on each of 4 postcards and had $1 left. How much did each postcard cost?

   $\$9 \div 4 = \$2 \ R\$1$; $2 each

Problem-Solving Applications: Mixed Review

Name _____

Date _____

Solve each problem and explain the method you used. If needed, do all your work on a separate sheet of paper.

Read ▸ **Plan** ▸ **Solve** ▸ **Check** ▸

Strategy File

Use These Strategies
Draw a Picture
Make a Table
Logical Reasoning
Use Simpler Numbers
Guess and Test

1. Mickey built a pyramid with 10 blocks. The fourth row has one block, while the second row has 2 more blocks than the fourth row. The base has 4 blocks. How many blocks are in the third row?

2 blocks

2. Amy spent $41.50 on movie tickets for 4 friends. About how much did each friend's ticket cost?

$41.50 → $40; $40 ÷ 4 = $10; about $10

3. Mrs. Wilson has 76 books. She puts them on 9 bookshelves. How many are on each shelf? How many books are left over?

76 ÷ 9 = 8 R4; 8 books per shelf; 4 left over

4. Harry's bamboo plant grows 2 in. a day. How much does it grow in a week?

2 in. × 7 = 14; 14 in.

5. Desiree has 87 guests at her wedding reception. If each table seats 7 people, how many tables are needed?

87 ÷ 7 = 12 R3; 13 tables

6. The product is 95. One factor is 5. What is the missing factor?

95 ÷ 5 = 19; 19

7. The dividend is 67. The divisor is 9. What are the quotient and remainder?

67 ÷ 9 = 7 R4; 7; 4

8. Jocelyn climbed three mountains. One was 4593 ft tall, one was 3655 ft tall, and one was 6445 ft tall. How tall were the mountains Jocelyn climbed in all?

4593 + 3655 + 6445 = 14,693; 14,693 feet

9. Four people were in a race. In what order did they finish if John is last, Laura finished just behind Tom, and Ty is in front of Laura?

1st-Ty, 2nd-Tom, 3rd-Laura, 4th-John

Fractions

Name _____

Date _____

Write the fraction for the shaded part.

1.

$\frac{1}{2}$

2.

$\frac{3}{5}$

3.

$\frac{2}{3}$

4.

$\frac{4}{6}$

Write each as a fraction.

5. one fourth ___ $\frac{1}{4}$ ___　　**6.** five eighths ___ $\frac{5}{8}$ ___　　**7.** three tenths ___ $\frac{3}{10}$ ___

8. four fifths ___ $\frac{4}{5}$ ___　　**9.** one third ___ $\frac{1}{3}$ ___　　**10.** two sixths ___ $\frac{2}{6}$ ___

11. six twelfths ___ $\frac{6}{12}$ ___　　**12.** seven tenths ___ $\frac{7}{10}$ ___　　**13.** one half ___ $\frac{1}{2}$ ___

Write the word name for each fraction.

14. $\frac{3}{8}$ ___ three eighths ___　　**15.** $\frac{9}{10}$ ___ nine tenths ___

16. $\frac{5}{6}$ ___ five sixths ___　　**17.** $\frac{2}{5}$ ___ two fifths ___

18. $\frac{2}{4}$ ___ two fourths ___　　**19.** $\frac{7}{8}$ ___ seven eighths ___

20. $\frac{7}{12}$ ___ seven twelfths ___　　**21.** $\frac{4}{9}$ ___ four ninths ___

Problem Solving

22. Which fraction names the larger
part: $\frac{1}{2}$ or $\frac{1}{8}$?

$\frac{1}{2}$

Equivalent Fractions

Name _____

Date _____

Equivalent fractions name the same amounts of a whole or of a set.

$$\frac{2}{3} = \frac{4}{6}$$

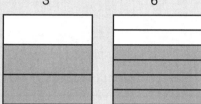

$$\frac{1}{3} = \frac{2}{6}$$

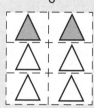

Shade the second figure so that it is equivalent to the first figure. Then write the equivalent fraction.

1.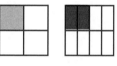

$$\frac{1}{4} = \frac{2}{8}$$

2.

$$\frac{5}{5} = \frac{10}{10}$$

3.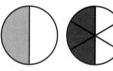

$$\frac{1}{2} = \frac{3}{6}$$

4.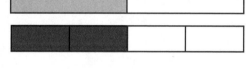

$$\frac{1}{2} = \frac{2}{4}$$

5.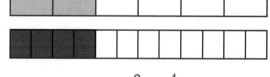

$$\frac{2}{6} = \frac{4}{12}$$

Write the equivalent fractions.

6.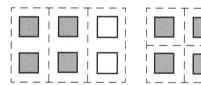

$$\frac{2}{3} = \frac{4}{6}$$

7.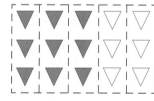

$$\frac{3}{5} = \frac{9}{15}$$

Write *Yes* or *No*.

8.

Does $\frac{1}{2} = \frac{2}{4}$? ___Yes___

9.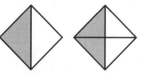

Does $\frac{2}{3} = \frac{3}{4}$? ___No___

10.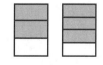

Does $\frac{1}{5} = \frac{2}{10}$? ___Yes___

Write the equivalent fraction for each.

11. $\frac{1}{3} = \frac{3}{9}$

12. $\frac{3}{4} = \frac{4}{12}$

13. $\frac{10}{12} = \frac{5}{6}$

Estimate Fractions

Name _____

Date _____

> Estimating using fractions tells you *about* how much.
>
>  about $\frac{1}{4}$ about $\frac{1}{2}$ about $\frac{3}{4}$

Is the estimate correct? Write *Yes* or *No*.

1. About what part is full?

Estimate: about $\frac{3}{4}$ ___Yes___

2. About how much is written on?

Estimate: about $\frac{1}{4}$ ___Yes___

3. About how much is white?

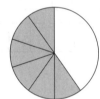

Estimate: about $\frac{1}{4}$ ___No___

4. About what part of the hour has passed?

Estimate: about $\frac{1}{2}$ ___No___

Estimate the fraction for the part of each set that is shaded. Write *less than $\frac{1}{2}$* or *more than $\frac{1}{2}$*.

5.

___ more than $\frac{1}{2}$

6.

less than $\frac{1}{2}$

7.

more than $\frac{1}{2}$

Estimate the time.

8.

about $\frac{1}{2}$ past three

9.

about $\frac{1}{4}$ past eight

10.

about $\frac{1}{4}$ to twelve

Compare Fractions

Name _____

Date _____

Compare: $\frac{5}{6}$ __?__ $\frac{3}{6}$

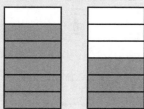

The denominators are the same.
Compare the numerators. 5 > 3

$$\frac{5}{6} > \frac{3}{6}$$

You can also use a number line to compare.

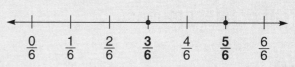

$\frac{5}{6}$ comes after $\frac{3}{6}$ on the number line.

$$\frac{5}{6} > \frac{3}{6}$$

Compare the fraction strips. Write < or >.

1.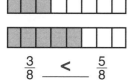

$$\frac{3}{8} \ \underline{<} \ \frac{5}{8}$$

2.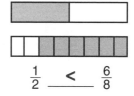

$$\frac{1}{2} \ \underline{<} \ \frac{6}{8}$$

Compare the fractions on each number line. Write < or >.

3.

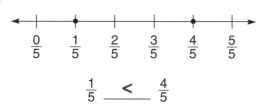

$$\frac{1}{5} \ \underline{<} \ \frac{4}{5}$$

4.

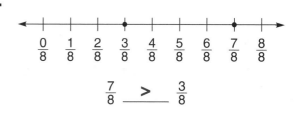

$$\frac{7}{8} \ \underline{>} \ \frac{3}{8}$$

Compare. Write < or >.

5. $\frac{3}{8} \ \underline{>} \ \frac{1}{4}$

6. $\frac{5}{6} \ \underline{>} \ \frac{2}{3}$

7. $\frac{3}{4} \ \underline{<} \ \frac{7}{8}$

8. $\frac{1}{6} \ \underline{<} \ \frac{2}{3}$

Problem Solving

9. The goal of the third grade was to raise $200 for a new volleyball net. Class A raised $\frac{6}{10}$ of the amount, and Class B raised $\frac{4}{10}$. Which class raised more?

$$\frac{6}{10} > \frac{4}{10} \text{ ; Class A}$$

10. Mary drank $\frac{3}{5}$ of a glass of milk. Peg drank $\frac{2}{5}$ of a glass of milk. Who drank less milk?

$$\frac{2}{5} < \frac{3}{5} \text{ ; Peg}$$

Order Fractions

Name _____

Date _____

Order $\frac{1}{2}$, $\frac{4}{6}$, $\frac{2}{6}$.

Write the fractions in order from greatest to least.

$\frac{4}{6}$, $\frac{1}{2}$, $\frac{2}{6}$

Write the fractions in order from least to greatest.

$\frac{2}{6}$, $\frac{1}{2}$, $\frac{4}{6}$

Compare your fraction models.

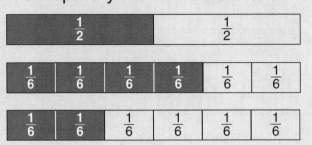

Write in order from least to greatest.

1. $\frac{3}{6}$ $\frac{5}{6}$ $\frac{2}{6}$

$\frac{2}{6}$, $\frac{3}{6}$, $\frac{5}{6}$

2. $\frac{3}{8}$ $\frac{2}{4}$ $\frac{5}{8}$

$\frac{3}{8}$, $\frac{2}{4}$, $\frac{5}{8}$

3. $\frac{4}{5}$ $\frac{3}{10}$ $\frac{9}{10}$

$\frac{3}{10}$, $\frac{4}{5}$, $\frac{9}{10}$

4. $\frac{1}{3}$ $\frac{5}{6}$ $\frac{1}{6}$

$\frac{1}{6}$, $\frac{1}{3}$, $\frac{5}{6}$

5. $\frac{1}{4}$ $\frac{3}{8}$ $\frac{1}{2}$

$\frac{1}{4}$, $\frac{3}{8}$, $\frac{1}{2}$

6. $\frac{1}{10}$ $\frac{1}{2}$ $\frac{1}{5}$

$\frac{1}{10}$, $\frac{1}{5}$, $\frac{1}{2}$

7. $\frac{4}{5}$ $\frac{7}{10}$ $\frac{3}{5}$

$\frac{3}{5}$, $\frac{7}{10}$, $\frac{4}{5}$

8. $\frac{1}{3}$ $\frac{1}{6}$ $\frac{3}{6}$

$\frac{1}{6}$, $\frac{1}{3}$, $\frac{3}{6}$

9. $\frac{5}{8}$ $\frac{1}{4}$ $\frac{1}{2}$

$\frac{1}{4}$, $\frac{1}{2}$, $\frac{5}{8}$

Write in order from greatest to least.

10. $\frac{3}{10}$ $\frac{2}{10}$ $\frac{4}{10}$

$\frac{4}{10}$, $\frac{3}{10}$, $\frac{2}{10}$

11. $\frac{1}{5}$ $\frac{3}{10}$ $\frac{2}{5}$

$\frac{2}{5}$, $\frac{3}{10}$, $\frac{1}{5}$

12. $\frac{5}{6}$ $\frac{1}{3}$ $\frac{2}{3}$

$\frac{5}{6}$, $\frac{2}{3}$, $\frac{1}{3}$

13. $\frac{1}{5}$ $\frac{5}{10}$ $\frac{3}{10}$

$\frac{5}{10}$, $\frac{3}{10}$, $\frac{1}{5}$

14. $\frac{1}{6}$ $\frac{4}{6}$ $\frac{1}{2}$

$\frac{4}{6}$, $\frac{1}{2}$, $\frac{1}{6}$

15. $\frac{1}{2}$ $\frac{3}{4}$ $\frac{7}{8}$

$\frac{7}{8}$, $\frac{3}{4}$, $\frac{1}{2}$

16. $\frac{1}{5}$ $\frac{1}{2}$ $\frac{6}{10}$

$\frac{6}{10}$, $\frac{1}{2}$, $\frac{1}{5}$

17. $\frac{5}{8}$ $\frac{2}{4}$ $\frac{3}{4}$

$\frac{3}{4}$, $\frac{5}{8}$, $\frac{2}{4}$

18. $\frac{1}{3}$ $\frac{1}{6}$ $\frac{2}{3}$

$\frac{2}{3}$, $\frac{1}{3}$, $\frac{1}{6}$

19. $\frac{2}{6}$ $\frac{5}{6}$ $\frac{2}{3}$

$\frac{5}{6}$, $\frac{2}{3}$, $\frac{2}{6}$

20. $\frac{3}{5}$ $\frac{4}{10}$ $\frac{1}{2}$

$\frac{3}{5}$, $\frac{1}{2}$, $\frac{4}{10}$

21. $\frac{1}{9}$ $\frac{8}{9}$ $\frac{2}{3}$

$\frac{8}{9}$, $\frac{2}{3}$, $\frac{1}{9}$

Find Part of a Set

Name _____

Date _____

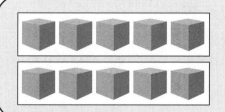 $\frac{1}{2}$ of 10 = _?_

Think: 10 ÷ 2 = 5   or $2\overline{)10}$ with 5

$\frac{1}{2}$ of 10 = 5

Find part of the set.

1. $\frac{1}{4}$ of 8 = __2__

2. $\frac{1}{3}$ of 9 = __3__

Find part of the number.

3. $\frac{1}{2}$ of 6 = __3__

6 ÷ 2 = __3__

4. $\frac{1}{3}$ of 3 = __1__

3 ÷ 3 = __1__

5. $\frac{1}{4}$ of 12 = __3__

12 ÷ 4 = __3__

6. $\frac{1}{2}$ of 12 = __6__

12 ÷ 2 = __6__

7. $\frac{1}{3}$ of 12 = __4__

12 ÷ 3 = __4__

8. $\frac{1}{6}$ of 24 = __4__

24 ÷ 6 = __4__

9. $\frac{1}{2}$ of 8 = __4__

10. $\frac{1}{3}$ of 21 = __7__

11. $\frac{1}{4}$ of 20 = __5__

12. $\frac{1}{10}$ of 50 = __5__

13. $\frac{1}{5}$ of 45 = __9__

14. $\frac{1}{5}$ of 40 = __8__

15. $\frac{1}{8}$ of 24 = __3__

16. $\frac{1}{6}$ of 18 = __3__

17. $\frac{1}{3}$ of 27 = __9__

Problem Solving

18. Which is shorter, $\frac{3}{4}$ of a foot, or 8 inches?

1 ft = 12 in.; $\frac{3}{4}$ of 12 in. = 9 in.; 8 in. < 9 in.; 8 in. is shorter

Mixed Numbers

Name _____

Date _____

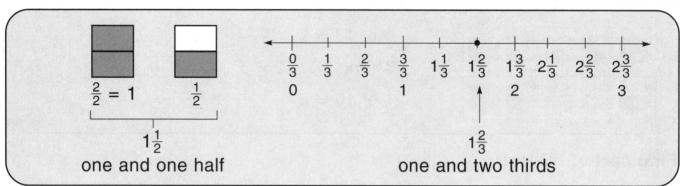

$\frac{2}{2} = 1$ $\frac{1}{2}$

$1\frac{1}{2}$
one and one half

$1\frac{2}{3}$
one and two thirds

Write the mixed number for each.

1.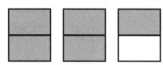

$2\frac{1}{2}$

2.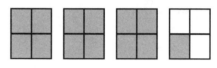

$3\frac{1}{4}$

3.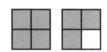

$1\frac{2}{5}$

4.

$1\frac{1}{4}$

Write the mixed number and word name for each.

5.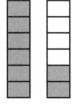

$1\frac{3}{4}$; one and three fourths

6.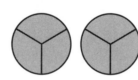

$2\frac{2}{3}$; two and two thirds

7.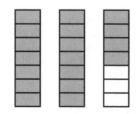

$1\frac{2}{6}$; one and two sixths

8.

$2\frac{4}{7}$; two and four sevenths

9.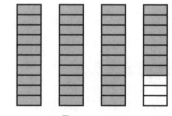

$3\frac{7}{10}$; three and seven tenths

Add Fractions

Name _____

Date _____

You can use fraction strips to add fractions.

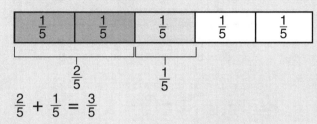

$$\frac{2}{5} + \frac{1}{5} = \frac{3}{5}$$

You can use a number line to add fractions.

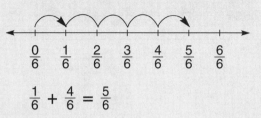

$$\frac{1}{6} + \frac{4}{6} = \frac{5}{6}$$

Shade each model to find the sum. Check student's shading.

1.

$\frac{1}{4}$	$\frac{1}{4}$	$\frac{1}{4}$	$\frac{1}{4}$

$\frac{1}{4} + \frac{2}{4} = \underline{\quad \frac{3}{4} \quad}$

2.

$\frac{1}{8}$	$\frac{1}{8}$	$\frac{1}{8}$	$\frac{1}{8}$	$\frac{1}{8}$	$\frac{1}{8}$	$\frac{1}{8}$	$\frac{1}{8}$

$\frac{2}{8} + \frac{3}{8} = \underline{\quad \frac{5}{8} \quad}$

3.

$\frac{1}{10}$	$\frac{1}{10}$	$\frac{1}{10}$	$\frac{1}{10}$	$\frac{1}{10}$	$\frac{1}{10}$	$\frac{1}{10}$	$\frac{1}{10}$	$\frac{1}{10}$	$\frac{1}{10}$

$\frac{5}{10} + \frac{4}{10} = \underline{\quad \frac{9}{10} \quad}$

Find the sum in simplest form. You may use fraction strips or a number line.

4. $\frac{1}{4} + \frac{1}{4} = \underline{\quad \frac{1}{2} \quad}$

5. $\frac{1}{10} + \frac{1}{10} = \underline{\quad \frac{1}{5} \quad}$

6. $\frac{1}{5} + \frac{1}{5} = \underline{\quad \frac{2}{5} \quad}$

7. $\frac{1}{6} + \frac{4}{6} = \underline{\quad \frac{5}{6} \quad}$

8. $\frac{3}{8} + \frac{4}{8} = \underline{\quad \frac{7}{8} \quad}$

9. $\frac{3}{10} + \frac{5}{10} = \underline{\quad \frac{4}{5} \quad}$

10. $\frac{5}{12} + \frac{2}{12} = \underline{\quad \frac{7}{12} \quad}$

11. $\frac{1}{8} + \frac{5}{8} = \underline{\quad \frac{3}{4} \quad}$

12. $\frac{2}{7} + \frac{2}{7} = \underline{\quad \frac{4}{7} \quad}$

Write an addition sentence to represent each number line.

13.

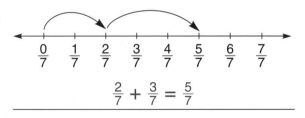

$$\frac{2}{7} + \frac{3}{7} = \frac{5}{7}$$

14.

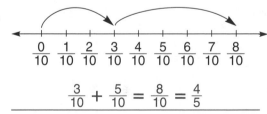

$$\frac{3}{10} + \frac{5}{10} = \frac{8}{10} = \frac{4}{5}$$

Problem Solving

15. Gerene bought $\frac{2}{8}$ yd of blue denim and $\frac{3}{8}$ yd of red denim. How much denim did she buy in all?

$\frac{2}{8} + \frac{3}{8} = \frac{5}{8}; \frac{5}{8}$ yd

Subtract Fractions

Name _____

Date _____

You can use fraction strips to subtract fractions.

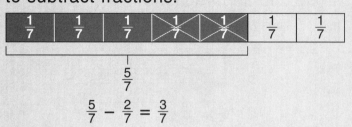

$$\frac{5}{7} - \frac{2}{7} = \frac{3}{7}$$

You can use a number line to subtract fractions.

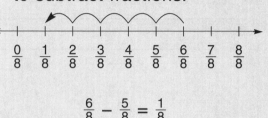

$$\frac{6}{8} - \frac{5}{8} = \frac{1}{8}$$

Shade each model and then draw Xs to find the difference. Check students' shading.

1.
$\frac{1}{3}$	$\frac{1}{3}$	$\frac{1}{3}$

$\frac{2}{3} - \frac{1}{3} = \underline{\quad \frac{1}{3} \quad}$

2.
$\frac{1}{10}$	$\frac{1}{10}$	$\frac{1}{10}$	$\frac{1}{10}$	$\frac{1}{10}$	$\frac{1}{10}$	$\frac{1}{10}$	$\frac{1}{10}$	$\frac{1}{10}$	$\frac{1}{10}$

$\frac{8}{10} - \frac{5}{10} = \underline{\quad \frac{3}{10} \quad}$

3.
$\frac{1}{12}$	$\frac{1}{12}$	$\frac{1}{12}$	$\frac{1}{12}$	$\frac{1}{12}$	$\frac{1}{12}$	$\frac{1}{12}$	$\frac{1}{12}$	$\frac{1}{12}$	$\frac{1}{12}$	$\frac{1}{12}$	$\frac{1}{12}$

$\frac{9}{12} - \frac{4}{12} = \underline{\quad \frac{5}{12} \quad}$

Find the difference in simplest form. You may use fraction strips or a number line.

4. $\frac{3}{4} - \frac{1}{4} = \underline{\quad \frac{1}{2} \quad}$

5. $\frac{5}{6} - \frac{3}{6} = \underline{\quad \frac{1}{3} \quad}$

6. $\frac{6}{7} - \frac{4}{7} = \underline{\quad \frac{2}{7} \quad}$

7. $\frac{7}{10} - \frac{6}{10} = \underline{\quad \frac{1}{10} \quad}$

8. $\frac{6}{8} - \frac{1}{8} = \underline{\quad \frac{5}{8} \quad}$

9. $\frac{4}{5} - \frac{2}{5} = \underline{\quad \frac{2}{5} \quad}$

10. $\frac{1}{2} - \frac{1}{2} = \underline{\quad 0 \quad}$

11. $\frac{7}{12} - \frac{3}{12} = \underline{\quad \frac{1}{3} \quad}$

12. $\frac{5}{8} - \frac{3}{8} = \underline{\quad \frac{1}{4} \quad}$

Write a subtraction sentence to represent each number line. Write the difference in simplest form.

13.
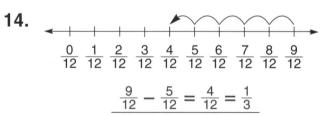

$$\frac{5}{5} - \frac{3}{5} = \frac{2}{5}$$

14.

$$\frac{9}{12} - \frac{5}{12} = \frac{4}{12} = \frac{1}{3}$$

Problem Solving You may use fraction strips.

15. Hector had $\frac{7}{8}$ cup of bleach. He used $\frac{4}{8}$ cup doing laundry. How much bleach was left?

$$\frac{7}{8} - \frac{4}{8} = \frac{3}{8}; \frac{3}{8} \text{ cup}$$

Unit Cost

> A bag of 4 apples costs 80¢.
> What is the unit cost of one apple?
>
> $\frac{1}{4}$ of 80¢ = _?_
>
> To find $\frac{1}{4}$ of 80¢, divide by 4.
>
> 80¢ ÷ 4 = 20¢
>
> The unit cost of one apple is 20¢.
>
> > Remember: $\frac{1}{4}$ means
> > 1 out of 4 equal parts.

Find the part of each amount.

1. $\frac{1}{6}$ of 36¢

    6¢

2. $\frac{1}{5}$ of 50¢

    10¢

3. $\frac{1}{7}$ of 49¢

    7¢

4. $\frac{1}{3}$ of 90¢

    30¢

5. $\frac{1}{9}$ of 72¢

    8¢

6. $\frac{1}{4}$ of 44¢

    11¢

7. $\frac{1}{2}$ of 68¢

    34¢

8. $\frac{1}{8}$ of 32¢

    4¢

9. $\frac{1}{3}$ of 45¢

    15¢

10. $\frac{1}{6}$ of 48¢

    8¢

11. $\frac{1}{9}$ of 27¢

    3¢

12. $\frac{1}{2}$ of 74¢

    37¢

13. $\frac{1}{4}$ of 36¢

    9¢

14. $\frac{1}{7}$ of 28¢

    4¢

15. $\frac{1}{3}$ of 54¢

    18¢

16. $\frac{1}{5}$ of 65¢

    13¢

Problem Solving

17. A 9-oz fruit cup is on sale for 63¢. Another brand of fruit cup that comes in a 7-oz jar is on sale for 56¢. Which fruit cup is the better buy?

    $\frac{1}{9}$ of 63¢ = 7¢; $\frac{1}{7}$ of 56¢ = 8¢
    7¢ < 8¢; 9-oz cup

18. A six-pack of juice costs 90¢. What is the unit cost of one can of juice?

    $\frac{1}{6}$ of 90¢ = 15¢; 15¢

Problem-Solving Strategy: Use a Drawing/Model

Name _____

Date _____

Jo drank 6 ounces of a 16-ounce bottle of apple juice. Did she drink more or less than $\frac{1}{2}$ the juice?

Since $\frac{1}{2}$ of 16 = 8, she drank less than $\frac{1}{2}$ of the juice.

Draw a picture:

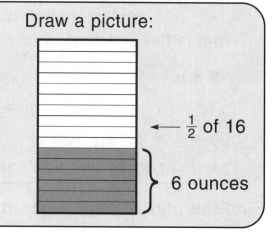

← $\frac{1}{2}$ of 16

} 6 ounces

Problem Solving Do your work on a separate sheet of paper.

1. Peter had 12 baseball cards. He traded $\frac{1}{3}$ of his cards with his cousin and $\frac{1}{4}$ of his cards with Tyrell. How many cards did he keep?

$\frac{1}{3}$ of 12 = 4; $\frac{1}{4}$ of 12 = 3;
3 + 4 = 7; 12 − 7 = 5; 5 cards

2. Jeanine went to the post office and bought 36 stamps. She used $\frac{1}{3}$ of the stamps to mail out invitations to her birthday party. How many stamps does she have left.

$\frac{1}{3}$ of 36 = 12; 36 − 12 = 24;
24 stamps

3. Juan's class went on a field trip in a bus. There were 32 seats, but $\frac{1}{4}$ of the seats were empty. How many seats were not empty?

$\frac{1}{4}$ of 32 = 8; 32 − 8 = 24; 24 seats

4. Hal's mother is sewing a blouse. She needs 2 yards of fabric. She has a piece of fabric 7 feet long. Does she have enough? (**Hint:** Remember there are 3 feet in 1 yard.)

2 yd = 6 ft; 7 ft > 6 ft; Yes

5. Norm and Liz used two sheets of plywood to make a doll house. They used $\frac{1}{4}$ of a sheet for the floors, $\frac{3}{4}$ of a sheet for the walls, and $\frac{1}{2}$ of a sheet for the roof. How much of the plywood was left?

$\frac{1}{4} + \frac{3}{4} = \frac{4}{4}$; $\frac{4}{4} = 1$;
$1 − \frac{1}{2} = \frac{1}{2}$; $\frac{1}{2}$ sheet

6. Molly plants 6 rosebushes in $\frac{1}{2}$ of her garden. She plants the same number of tulips, irises, and lilies as rosebushes in the other half of her garden. How many tulips, irises, and lilies did she plant in all?

6 + 6 + 6 = 18; 18

Problem-Solving Application: Mixed Review

Name _____

Date _____

Solve each problem and explain the method you used. If needed, do all your work on a separate sheet of paper.

Read ▶ Plan ▶ Solve ▶ Check ▶

Strategy File

Use These Strategies
Use More Than One Step
Use a Graph
Use a Drawing/Model
Choose the Operation
Logical Reasoning

1. Haley bought a 12-pack of gum. He gave $\frac{1}{6}$ of the pack to Martha. How many pieces of gum does Haley have left?

   $\frac{1}{6}$ of 12 = 2; 12 − 2 = 10;
   10 pieces

2. There are 39 cars in the parking lot. $\frac{1}{3}$ of them are silver and the rest are other colors. How many of the cars in the parking lot are other colors?

   $\frac{1}{3}$ of 39 = 13; 39 − 13 = 26; 26 cars

3. Hank has finished $\frac{7}{9}$ of his homework. Billy has finished $\frac{2}{3}$ of his homework. Who is closer to finishing his homework?

   $\frac{2}{3} = \frac{6}{9}$; $\frac{7}{9} > \frac{6}{9}$; Hank

4. $\frac{7}{10}$ of the people who take the biology test get passing grades. If 20 people take the test, how many get passing grades?

   $\frac{7}{10}$ of 20 = 14; 14 people

5. Marcel, Josh, and Clara ate a whole pie. Marcel ate $\frac{1}{5}$ of it, Clara ate $\frac{1}{2}$ of it, and Josh ate the rest. Who ate the least amount of pie?

   $\frac{1}{5} = \frac{2}{10}$; $\frac{1}{2} = \frac{5}{10}$; $\frac{2}{10} + \frac{5}{10} = \frac{7}{10}$;
   $1 - \frac{7}{10} = \frac{3}{10}$; $\frac{2}{10} < \frac{3}{10} < \frac{5}{10}$; Marcel

6. Barney made 16 tacos for a dinner party. Each guest ate 2 tacos. Altogether they ate $\frac{1}{2}$ the tacos. How many guests were at the party?

   $\frac{1}{2}$ of 16 = 8; 8 ÷ 2 = 4; 4 guests

7. There are 8 members in the Lopez family. $\frac{1}{4}$ of them play golf, and the rest play tennis. How many play golf? How many play tennis?

   $\frac{1}{4}$ of 8 = 2; 8 − 2 = 6; 2 play golf;
   6 play tennis

8. Joe's Plumbing unclogged 16 drains today. $\frac{1}{8}$ of the jobs were clogged sinks, and the rest were clogged showers. How many clogged sinks did they fix? How many showers?

   $\frac{1}{8}$ of 16 = 2; 16 − 2 = 14; 2 clogged sinks; 14 clogged showers

9. It takes Melissa 20 minutes to get to school. It takes Karin $\frac{1}{2}$ an hour to get to school. How long do they travel in all?

   1 hr = 60 min; $\frac{1}{2}$ of 60 = 30;
   20 + 30 = 50; 50 minutes

Fractions and Decimals

Name _____

Date _____

 $\frac{1}{10} = 0.1$
one tenth

 $\frac{4}{10} = 0.4$
four tenths

 $\frac{8}{10} = 0.8$
eight tenths

Write the fraction and the decimal for the shaded part of each.

1. 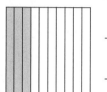 $\frac{3}{10}$

0.3

2.  $\frac{9}{10}$

0.9

3.  $\frac{5}{10}$

0.5

Write the word name for each.

4. $\frac{2}{10}$ __two tenths__

5. $\frac{5}{10}$ __five tenths__

6. $\frac{9}{10}$ __nine tenths__

7. 0.3 __three tenths__

8. 0.4 __four tenths__

9. 0.7 __seven tenths__

Write as a decimal.

10. $\frac{3}{10}$ __0.3__

11. $\frac{8}{10}$ __0.8__

12. $\frac{7}{10}$ __0.7__

13. $\frac{6}{10}$ __0.6__

14. two tenths __0.2__

15. four tenths __0.4__

16. five tenths __0.5__

17. nine tenths __0.9__

Complete this number line for fractions and decimals.

18.

| 0 | 0.1 | 0.2 | 0.3 | 0.4 | 0.5 | 0.6 | 0.7 | 0.8 | 0.9 | 1.0 |

| $\frac{0}{10}$ | $\frac{1}{10}$ | $\frac{2}{10}$ | $\frac{3}{10}$ | $\frac{4}{10}$ | $\frac{5}{10}$ | $\frac{6}{10}$ | $\frac{7}{10}$ | $\frac{8}{10}$ | $\frac{9}{10}$ | $\frac{10}{10}$ |

Problem Solving Write the answer as a fraction and as a decimal.

19. The Wolves won seven tenths of their baseball games. What part of the games did the team win? _____ $\frac{7}{10}$; 0.7

20. The Lions won five tenths of their games. What part of the games did the team win? _____ $\frac{5}{10}$; 0.5

Hundredths

$$\frac{55}{100} = 0.55$$

Read $\frac{55}{100}$ and 0.55 as fifty-five hundredths.

Write the fraction and the decimal for each shaded part.

1. 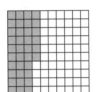 $\frac{36}{100}$

0.36

2. $\frac{71}{100}$

0.71

3. $\frac{49}{100}$

0.49

Write as a decimal.

4. $\frac{68}{100}$ ____ 0.68

5. $\frac{24}{100}$ ____ 0.24

6. $\frac{18}{100}$ ____ 0.18

7. seventy-three hundredths ____ 0.73 ____

8. fifty hundredths ____ 0.50 ____

9. eight hundredths ____ 0.08 ____

10. sixteen hundredths ____ 0.16 ____

Write the fraction and word name for each.

11. 0.71 $\frac{71}{100}$

seventy-one hundredths

12. 0.04 $\frac{4}{100}$

four hundredths

13. 0.92 $\frac{92}{100}$

ninety-two hundredths

14. 0.88 $\frac{88}{100}$

eighty-eight hundredths

15. 0.10 $\frac{10}{100}$

ten hundredths

16. 0.26 $\frac{26}{100}$

twenty-six hundredths

Write the word name for each.

17. $\frac{6}{100}$ ____ six hundredths ____

18. 0.95 ____ ninety-five hundredths

Problem Solving Write the answer as a fraction and as a decimal.

19. Robin had a box of 100 greeting cards. She sent 41 cards to her friends during the holidays. What part of the cards did she send?

____ $\frac{41}{100}$; 0.41

Decimals Greater Than One

Name _____

Date _____

 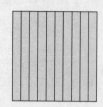 

1 whole   1 whole $\frac{3}{10}$

Mixed Number: $2\frac{3}{10}$
Decimal: 2.3
Read: two and three tenths

Write the mixed number and the decimal for each.

1.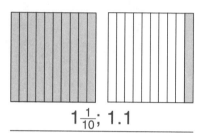

$1\frac{1}{10}$; 1.1

2.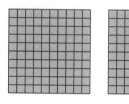

$1\frac{33}{100}$; 1.33

Write the decimal and word name for each.

3. $6\frac{9}{10}$ _____6.9; six and nine tenths_____

4. $7\frac{7}{10}$ _____7.7; seven and seven tenths_____

5. $5\frac{4}{10}$ _____5.4; five and four tenths_____

6. $1\frac{65}{100}$ _____1.65; one and sixty-five hundredths_____

7. $9\frac{6}{100}$ _____9.06; nine and six hundredths_____

8. $3\frac{12}{100}$ _____3.12; three and twelve hundredths_____

Complete each number line.

9.
5.1 | 5.2 5.3 5.4 | 5.5 | 5.6 5.7 5.8 5.9 | 6.0 | 6.1 6.2 6.3 6.4 | 6.5

10.
6.6 | 6.7 6.8 6.9 7.0 | 7.1 | 7.2 7.3 7.4 7.5 7.6 | 7.7 | 7.8 7.9 | 8.0

Write *Yes* or *No*.

11. Does $1\frac{8}{10} = 1.9$? _____No_____

12. Does $3\frac{5}{10} = 3.5$? _____Yes_____

13. Does $2\frac{2}{10} = 2.02$? _____No_____

14. Does $6\frac{4}{100} = 6.04$? _____Yes_____

Compare and Order Decimals

Compare: 2.4 _?_ 2.7

Think: 2.4 is to the left of 2.7

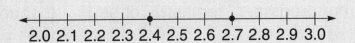

2.0 2.1 2.2 2.3 2.4 2.5 2.6 2.7 2.8 2.9 3.0

2.4 is less than 2.7.

So 2.4 < 2.7.

Compare. Write < or >. You may use a number line.

1. 0.3 ___>___ 0.1

2. 0.2 ___>___ 0.1

3. 0.7 ___<___ 0.9

4. $\frac{2}{10}$ ___<___ 0.6

5. 0.8 ___>___ $\frac{7}{10}$

6. $\frac{3}{10}$ ___<___ 0.5

7. $\frac{9}{10}$ ___>___ 0.1

8. 0.8 ___>___ $\frac{6}{10}$

9. 2.3 ___<___ 2.6

10. 1.5 ___>___ 1.3

11. 3.9 ___>___ 3.2

12. 7.8 ___>___ 7.0

13. 6.5 ___<___ 9.3

14. 8.4 ___>___ 2.2

15. 3.1 ___>___ 1.3

Order from least to greatest. You may use a number line.

16. 0.3, 0.5, 0.1 _____ 0.1, 0.3, 0.5 _____

17. 4.4, 4.5, 4.0 _____ 4.0, 4.4, 4.5 _____

18. 6.1, 6.7, 6.5 _____ 6.1, 6.5, 6.7 _____

Problem Solving

19. Marie ran 2.3 miles while training for a race. David ran 2.7 miles. Who ran the greater distance?

_____ 2.7 > 2.3; David _____

20. Brooke walked 0.8 mile on Monday. She walked 0.6 mile on Wednesday. On which day did she walk farther?

_____ 0.8 > 0.6; Monday _____

Use with Lesson 13-4, text pages 422–423.

Add and Subtract Decimals

Name _____

Date _____

Add hundredths.	Add tenths.	Add ones.	Subtract hundredths.	Subtract tenths.	Subtract ones.
3.75 +2.53 —— 8	3.75 +2.53 —— 28	¹ 3.75 +2.53 —— 6.28	⁷¹⁵ 6.8̄5̄ −3.17 —— 8	⁷¹⁵ 6.8̄5̄ −3.17 —— 68	⁷¹⁵ 6.8̄5̄ −3.17 —— 3.68

Find the sum.

1. 1.6 +2.2 —— 3.8	**2.** 7.2 +1.4 —— 8.6	**3.** 24.7 +13.4 —— 38.1	**4.** 4.03 +1.92 —— 5.95	**5.** 4.76 +1.63 —— 6.39
6. 2.5 3.7 +7.4 —— 13.6	**7.** 4.5 5.5 +8.6 —— 18.6	**8.** 3.21 6.83 +2.84 —— 12.88	**9.** 4.11 3.23 +1.83 —— 9.17	**10.** 7.14 4.36 +2.15 —— 13.65

Find the difference.

11. 5.8 −3.2 —— 2.6	**12.** 8.3 −2.7 —— 5.6	**13.** 8.63 −4.01 —— 4.62	**14.** 8.84 −2.63 —— 6.21	**15.** 7.62 −5.39 —— 2.23
16. 6.78 −3.46 —— 3.32	**17.** 8.50 −3.41 —— 5.09	**18.** 9.32 −1.88 —— 7.44	**19.** 53.27 −14.08 —— 39.19	**20.** 63.26 −12.83 —— 50.43

Add or subtract. Watch for + and − signs.

21. 2.89 +5.70 —— 8.59	**22.** 6.80 −4.37 —— 2.43	**23.** 7.10 −2.47 —— 4.63	**24.** 9.00 +3.48 —— 12.48	**25.** 1.90 +5.57 —— 7.47

Problem Solving

26. Nahoko is training for a cross country race. She ran 2.8 miles on Saturday and 3.2 miles on Sunday. How much farther did she run on Sunday than on Saturday?

3.2 − 2.8 = 0.4; 0.4 mi

Multiply Money

Name _____

Date _____

What is the total cost of 4 pairs of socks?

Estimate: 4 × $2.00 = $8.00

$2.39

Multiply:

```
    1 3
  $2.39
×     4
  $9.56
```

Write $ and .
in the product.

Four pairs of socks cost $9.56.

Estimate by rounding. Then multiply. Accept reasonable estimates.

1.
```
  $.72
×    4
```
$2.80; $2.88

2.
```
  $.37
×    2
```
$.80; $.74

3.
```
  $2.83
×     3
```
$9.00; $8.49

4.
```
  $3.60
×     2
```
$8.00; $7.20

5.
```
  $1.74
×     4
```
$8.00; $6.96

6.
```
  $.45
×    5
```
$2.50; $2.25

7.
```
  $.28
×    6
```
$1.80; $1.68

8.
```
  $4.53
×     3
```
$15.00; $13.59

9.
```
  $2.76
×     6
```
$18.00; $16.56

10.
```
  $5.69
×     4
```
$24.00; $22.76

Multiply.

11.
```
  $.60
×    3
 $1.80
```

12.
```
  $.75
×    4
 $3.00
```

13.
```
  $1.85
×     5
 $9.25
```

14.
```
  $3.56
×     6
 $21.36
```

15.
```
  $4.89
×     3
 $14.67
```

16.
```
  $.78
×    2
 $1.56
```

17.
```
  $.98
×    4
 $3.92
```

18.
```
  $3.80
×     5
 $19.00
```

19.
```
  $2.54
×     6
 $15.24
```

20.
```
  $1.97
×     7
 $13.79
```

21. 7 × $9.63
$67.41

22. 3 × $.67
$2.01

23. 5 × $7.05
$35.25

Problem Solving

24. Maidee sold 6 large shell bracelets for $2.45 each. What was the total cost?   6 × $2.45 = $14.70; $14.70

25. Jason sold 8 small bracelets for $1.98 each and 5 large ones for $6.75. How much money did he make in all?

8 × $1.98 = $15.84;
5 × $6.75 = $33.75;
$15.84 + 33.75 = $49.59; $49.59

Divide Money

Name _____

Date _____

How much does one apple cost?

Divide:

$$
\begin{array}{r}
\$\ .30 \\
6\overline{)\$1.80} \\
-18 \\
\hline
0 \\
-0 \\
\hline
-0
\end{array}
$$

Bring up the decimal point in the quotient. Then write the $ sign.

6 for $1.80

One apple costs $.30.

Divide and check. If needed, do your work on a separate sheet of paper.

1. $\dfrac{\$.44}{2\overline{)\$.88}}$

2. $\dfrac{\$.23}{3\overline{)\$.69}}$

3. $\dfrac{\$.30}{2\overline{)\$.60}}$

4. $\dfrac{\$.20}{5\overline{)\$1.00}}$

5. $\dfrac{\$1.20}{2\overline{)\$2.40}}$

6. $\dfrac{\$3.13}{3\overline{)\$9.39}}$

7. $\dfrac{\$.61}{4\overline{)\$2.44}}$

8. $\dfrac{\$2.00}{5\overline{)\$10.00}}$

9. $\dfrac{\$.24}{2\overline{)\$.48}}$

10. $\dfrac{\$.12}{5\overline{)\$.60}}$

11. $\dfrac{\$2.29}{4\overline{)\$9.16}}$

12. $\dfrac{\$\ .55}{5\overline{)\$2.75}}$

13. $\dfrac{\$1.40}{6\overline{)\$8.40}}$

14. $\dfrac{\$2.78}{3\overline{)\$8.34}}$

15. $\dfrac{\$1.24}{4\overline{)\$4.96}}$

16. $\dfrac{\$1.62}{6\overline{)\$9.72}}$

17. $\$.96 \div 8 = \underline{\$.12}$

18. $\$.70 \div 5 = \underline{\$.14}$

19. $\$4.00 \div 2 = \underline{\$2.00}$

20. $\$6.30 \div 3 = \underline{\$2.10}$

21. $\$9.12 \div 6 = \underline{\$1.52}$

22. $\$8.56 \div 4 = \underline{\$2.14}$

Problem Solving

23. Three T-shirts come in a package that costs $6.75. What is the cost of one T-shirt?

   $\$6.75 \div 3 = \$2.25; \$2.25$

24. Eight headbands come in a bag that costs $7.60. What is the cost of one headband?

   $\$7.60 \div 8 = \$.95; \$.95$

Problem-Solving Strategy: Find a Pattern

Name _____

Date _____

What numbers come next in the pattern:

4.2, 4.5, 4.3, 4.6, 4.4, 4.7, 4.5, __?__, __?__

4.2		4.5		4.3		4.6		4.4
	+0.3		−0.2		+0.3		−0.2	

Think: Make a table and look for a pattern.

The next two numbers are 4.8, 4.6.

Solve. Do your work on a separate sheet of paper.

1. Yoshi's combination lock must be turned 8 times in a pattern. The first four turns are: 8.1, 7.2, 6.3, 5.4. What is the pattern? What are the last four turns?

   _____−0.9; 4.5, 3.6, 2.7, 1.8_____

2. The flight time in a small plane from Cairo to Casablanca is 6.5 hr. Every 0.5 hr the pilot must report the plane's location. How many times is the location reported?

   _____13 times_____

3. Bettina lifts 3.6 lb the first day, 3.7 lb the second day, 3.9 lb the third day, 4.2 lb the fourth day and 4.6 lb the fifth day, and so on. On what day will she lift *more than* 8 lb?

   _____10th day-8.1 lb_____

4. What number comes next in Jack's pattern?

   5.2, 5.0, 5.5, 5.3, 5.8, 5.6, 6.1

   _____−0.2, +0.5; 5.9_____

5. Yao and Jill sold brownies. The first week they sold 1.5 dozen. Every week they sold 1.5 dozen more than the week before. How many brownies did they sell the fifth week?

   _____7.5 dozen_____

6. Sarah can walk one block in 1.2 min. She can run one block in 0.7 min. If she alternates running one block and walking one block, how many blocks can she go in 7.6 min?

   _____8 blocks_____

Problem-Solving Applications: Mixed Review

Name _____

Date _____

Solve each problem and explain the method you used. If needed, do all your work on a separate sheet of paper.

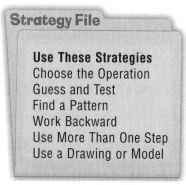

1. The old state record for a race was 49.7 seconds. Manny beat the record by 1.6 seconds. What was Manny's time?

   49.7 − 1.6 = 48.1; 48.1 seconds

2. Gino ran 5.4 miles on Tuesday, and 6.8 miles on Wednesday. How many miles did he run altogether?

   5.4 + 6.8 = 12.2; 12.2 miles

3. Natalie ate 0.6 of a pizza. Did she eat more or less than $\frac{2}{5}$ of the pizza?

   $\frac{2}{5}$ = 0.4; 0.4 < 0.6; more than $\frac{2}{5}$

4. Dr. Johnson ran 3.1 miles on Monday, 3.4 miles on Tuesday, and 3.7 miles on Wednesday. If this pattern continues, how many miles will she run Saturday?

   4.6 miles

5. Phil's dad gave him money to go to a baseball game. The ticket was $5.25, a hot dog was $1.50, and a drink was $2.20. If Phil had $2.05 left over, how much money did his dad give him?

   $5.25 + $1.50 + $2.20 + $2.05 = $11; $11

6. Marcella lives 7.1 miles directly west of school. Enrico lives 6.3 miles directly east of school. How far do they live from each other?

   7.1 + 6.3 = 13.4; 13.4 miles

7. Henry used a coupon for $1.10 when buying a box of cereal. He paid $3.85. What was the price of the cereal before the coupon?

   $3.85 + $1.10 = $4.95; $4.95

8. Sandy spent $11.25 at the grocery store on smoothies and bananas. The bananas cost $3.25 less than the smoothies. How much did each cost?

   $7.25 − 4 = $3.25; $7.25 + 4 = $11.25; smoothies-$7.25; bananas-$4

9. Marisa got .85 of the problems on her math test correct. Jill got $\frac{20}{25}$ questions correct. Who got a better grade on the test?

   $\frac{20}{25}$ = .80; .80 < .85; Marisa

Divisibility

Name _____

Date _____

$10 \div 2 = 5$	$10 \div 5 = 2$	$10 \div 10 = 1$
Any number ending in 0, 2, 4, 6, or 8 is *divisible* by 2.	Any number ending in 0 or 5 is *divisible* by 5.	Any number ending in 0 is *divisible* by 10.

Is the number divisible by 2? Write *Yes* or *No*.

1. 4 __Yes__   **2.** 35 __No__   **3.** 40 __Yes__   **4.** 59 __No__

5. 213 __No__   **6.** 754 __Yes__   **7.** 1002 __Yes__   **8.** 6365 __No__

Is the number divisible by 5? Write *Yes* or *No*.

9. 20 __Yes__   **10.** 32 __No__   **11.** 55 __Yes__   **12.** 67 __No__

13. 395 __Yes__   **14.** 521 __No__   **15.** 1080 __Yes__   **16.** 4489 __No__

Is the number divisible by 10? Write *Yes* or *No*.

17. 15 __No__   **18.** 50 __Yes__   **19.** 48 __No__   **20.** 99 __No__

21. 205 __No__   **22.** 330 __Yes__   **23.** 7700 __Yes__   **24.** 1001 __No__

Complete the table. Write *Yes* or *No*.

	Divisible by	20	35	68	92	110	3152
25.	2	Yes	No	Yes	Yes	Yes	Yes
26.	5	Yes	Yes	No	No	Yes	No
27.	10	Yes	No	No	No	Yes	No

Problem Solving

28. I am a number that is divisible by 2, 5, and 10. I am between 35 and 45. What number am I?   ____40____

Expressions and Variables

An expression has only numbers and operation signs.	A variable is a letter that stands for an unknown number.
$36 \div 3$ 4×5 $15 - 6$	$26 + n$
↑ ↑ ↑ expressions	↑ variable

Tell whether each is an expression or a number sentence.

1. 28×9

___expression___

2. $44 \div 4$

___expression___

3. $22 - 8 = 14$

___number sentence___

4. $55 - 25$

___expression___

5. $12 + 7 = 19$

___number sentence___

6. $23 + 11 = 34$

___number sentence___

Write an expression for each word phrase.
Use the letter *n* as a variable for any unknown number.

7. 80 minus 25

___$80 - 25$___

8. a number divided by 12

___$n \div 12$___

9. the sum of 8 and a number

___$8 + n$___

10. 6 times five

___6×5___

11. a difference of 43 and 12

___$43 - 12$___

12. sixty plus 4204

___$60 + 4204$___

13. 9 times a number

___$9 \times n$___

14. 6.2 added to 9.7

___$9.7 + 6.2$___

Problem Solving

Write an expression for each situation.

15. Marcus ran 2.5 miles and cycled 1.2 miles. How many miles did he travel altogether?

___$2.5 + 1.2$___

16. Robbie made 28 cookies. He gave some to Annie. How many cookies does he have left?

___$28 - n$___

Order of Operations

Name _____

Date _____

Simplify: 3 + 2 × 4

> Multiply or divide in order from left to right.
> Add or subtract in order from left to right.

So 3 + 2 × 4 = 11.

$$3 + 2 \times 4$$
$$3 + \quad 8$$
$$11$$

Write the letter of the operation that should be done first.
Then compute.

a. addition	b. subtraction
c. multiplication	d. division

1. 7 + 4 − 2 _____a; 9_____   **2.** 63 − 2 + 5 _____b; 66_____

3. 53 − 4 × 2 _____c; 45_____   **4.** 15 ÷ 5 × 2 _____d; 6_____

5. 3 + 4 − 1 × 6 _____c; 1_____   **6.** 8 − 2 × 3 ÷ 3 _____c; 6_____

7. 5 × 3 + 7 = _____c; 22_____   **8.** 6 + 8 × 2 = _____c; 22_____

9. 6 + 6 ÷ 2 = _____d; 9_____   **10.** 12 ÷ 3 + 4 = _____d; 8_____

11. 36 − 15 ÷ 5 = _____d; 33_____   **12.** 48 − 36 ÷ 4 = _____d; 39_____

13. 10 ÷ 2 + 9 ÷ 1 = _____d; 14_____   **14.** 32 ÷ 4 − 4 ÷ 2 = _____d; 6_____

15. 6 × 4 − 8 ÷ 2 = _____c; 20_____   **16.** 27 ÷ 9 + 5 × 1 = _____d; 8_____

17. 15 ÷ 3 + 8 ÷ 1 = _____d; 13_____   **18.** 6 × 3 − 28 ÷ 7 = _____c; 14_____

Missing Operation

Name _____

Date _____

> **Use Guess and Test to find the missing operation.**
>
> | 6 ? 9 = 54 | 12 ? 7 = 5 |
> |---|---|
> | **Think:** 54 is greater than both 6 and 9. | **Think:** 5 is less than both 7 and 12. |
> | Guess addition or multiplication. | Guess subtraction or division. |
> | **Test:** 6 + 9 = 54 not true
 6 × 9 = 54 true | **Test:** 12 ÷ 7 = 5 not true
 12 − 7 = 5 true |

Write + or − to complete.

1. 8 $+$ 5 = 13   2. 6 $+$ 6 = 12   3. 13 $-$ 6 = 7   4. 7 $-$ 7 = 0

5. 6 $+$ 4 = 10   6. 6 $+$ 3 = 9   7. 5 $+$ 5 = 10   8. 8 $+$ 2 = 10

9. 9 $+$ 1 = 10   10. 14 $-$ 8 = 6   11. 9 $+$ 6 = 15   12. 17 $-$ 9 = 8

Write × or ÷ to complete.

13. 5 $\times$ 8 = 40   14. 56 $\div$ 7 = 8   15. 6 $\times$ 4 = 24   16. 2 $\times$ 9 = 18

17. 3 $\div$ 3 = 1   18. 35 $\div$ 7 = 5   19. 4 $\times$ 7 = 28   20. 1 $\times$ 7 = 7

21. 30 $\div$ 6 = 5   22. 18 $\div$ 3 = 6   23. 9 $\times$ 5 = 45   24. 0 $\times$ 8 = 0 <br> or ÷

Write +, −, ×, or ÷ to complete.

25. 14 $-$ 7 = 7   26. 8 $+$ 4 = 12   27. 4 $\times$ 4 = 16   28. 12 $\div$ 3 = 4

29. 9 $-$ 8 = 1   30. 2 $\times$ 4 = 8   31. 42 $\div$ 7 = 6   32. 8 $\times$ 8 = 64

Problem Solving

33. Margaret's swim team practices for 2 hours each day from Monday to Friday. How many hours do they practice in one week?

2 × 5 = 10; 10h

Factors

Name _____

Date _____

Use multiplication sentences to find the factors of a number
and the common factors of two or more numbers.

Factors of 8: **1, 2**, 4, 8	Factors of 6: **1, 2**, 3, 6	Common factors
$1 \times 8 = 8$	$1 \times 6 = 6$	of 6 and 8:
$2 \times 4 = 8$	$2 \times 3 = 6$	**1, 2**

Find all the factors of each number.
You may use multiplication sentences.

1. 16 _____ 1, 2, 4, 8, 16 _____

2. 10 _____ 1, 2, 5, 10 _____

3. 28 _____ 1, 2, 4, 7, 14, 28 _____

4. 24 _____ 1, 2, 3, 4, 6, 12, 24 _____

5. 18 _____ 1, 2, 3, 6, 9, 18 _____

6. 20 _____ 1, 2, 4, 5, 10, 20 _____

7. 32 _____ 1, 2, 4, 8, 16, 32 _____

8. 36 _____ 1, 2, 3, 4, 6, 9, 12, 18, 36 _____

List all the common factors of each set of numbers.

9. 8 and 16 ___ 1, 2, 4, 8 ___

10. 21 and 27 ___ 1, 3 ___

11. 12 and 16 ___ 1, 2, 4 ___

12. 8 and 12 ___ 1, 2, 4 ___

13. 20 and 40 ___ 1, 2, 5, 10, 20 ___

14. 15 and 30 ___ 1, 3, 5, 15 ___

15. 9 and 24 ___ 1, 3 ___

16. 10 and 40 ___ 1, 2, 5, 10 ___

17. 16 and 24 ___ 1, 2, 4, 8 ___

18. 18 and 30 ___ 1, 2, 3, 6 ___

Number Sentences

Name _____

Date _____

$55 + 30 - 5 = 2 \bigcirc n$
- First find the value on the left side: $55 + 30 - 5 = 2 \bigcirc n$
                                                    $80 = 2 \bigcirc n$

- Then use guess and test for the right side
  to find the missing operation and number.

  $80 = 2 \bigcirc n$ $80 = 2 \bigcirc n$

  $80 = 2 \oplus 78$ $80 = 2 \otimes 40$

So $+78$ or $\times 4$ will make the expressions equal.

Solve the left side of the equation.
Then find two ways to make the sides equal in value.

1. $27 + 13 - 10 = 1 \bigcirc n$

       $30; \times 30, +29$

2. $512 - 470 + 3 = 90 \bigcirc n$

       $45; \div 2, -45$

3. $16 + 50 - 2 = 128 \bigcirc n$

       $64; \div 2, -64$

4. $62 - 37 + 5 = 5 \bigcirc n$

       $30; \times 6, +25$

5. $28 - 23 + 7 = 2 \bigcirc n$

       $12; \times 6, +10$

6. $72 - 17 + 5 = 120 \bigcirc n$

       $60; \div 2, -60$

Find whole numbers that make each sentence true.

7. $34 \div 2 > n \times 2$

       numbers ≤ 8

8. $25 \times 4 < 10 + n$

       numbers ≥ 91

9. $65 + n < 15 \times 5$

       numbers ≤ 9

10. $270 \div 9 > 35 - n$

       numbers ≥ 6

11. $320 \div 8 > n - 5$

       numbers ≤ 44

12. $75 + 15 < n \times 9$

       numbers ≥ 11

13. $13 \times 6 > n + 18$

       numbers ≤ 59

14. $65 - 60 > n \div 3$

       numbers ≤ 14

Problem-Solving Strategy: Use More Than One Step

Name _____

Date _____

Arlene wanted to make fruit salad for the party. She bought apples for $7.18, bananas for $6.42, and pears for $9.77. How much change did she get from $30.00?

Arlene's change was $6.63.

Think: Add $7.18 + $6.42 + $9.77. Subtract the sum from $30.00 to find how much Arlene has left.

```
  1  1                    9 9
$7. 1 8            2 1̸0 1̸0 10
  6. 4 2            $3̸ 0̸. 0̸ 0̸
+ 9. 7 7           − 2 3. 3 7
$2 3. 3 7          $   6. 6 3
```

Solve. Do your work on a separate sheet of paper.

1. Daisy sold 9 apple dumplings for a total of $11.25. Each dumpling cost $0.75 to make. How much profit did Daisy make from selling her dumplings?

   9 × $.75 = $6.75;
   $11.25 − $6.75 = $4.50;
   $4.50 profit

2. Melissa scored 48 points in a video game. Then she doubled her points. Andre scored 31 points and then tripled his points. Who had a higher score?

   2 × 48 = 96; 3 × 31 = 93;
   96 > 93; Melissa

3. Cherries are $1.29 a pound. Randy buys 5 pounds of cherries to make jelly. How much change will he get from a ten-dollar bill?

   5 × $1.29 = $6.45;
   $10.00 − $6.45 = $3.55; $3.55

4. A rectangular sign is twice as long as it is wide. It is 15 feet wide. What is the perimeter of the sign?

   2 × 15 = 30 ft;
   15 + 15 + 30+ 30 = 90; 90 ft

5. Cereal X has 3 times more oats than Cereal Y, which has 2 times more oats than Cereal Z. If Cereal X has 30 ounces of oats, how many ounces of oats are in Cereal Z?

   30 ÷ 3 = 10; 10 ÷ 2 = 5; 5 oz

6. Miguel needs to earn $35.00 for a camping trip. If he mows lawns for 3 days and earns $7.95 each day and rakes leaves for 2 days at $5.00 per day, will he earn enough money?

   3 × $7.95 = $23.85;
   2 × $5.00 = $10.00;
   $23.85 + $10.00 = $33.85; No

Problem-Solving Applications: Mixed Review

Name _____

Date _____

Solve each problem and explain the method you used. If needed, do all your work on a separate sheet of paper.

Read Plan Solve Check

Strategy File

Use These Strategies
Use More Than One Step
Find a Pattern
Use a Drawing or Model
Choose the Operation
Interpret the Remainder
Guess and Test

1. Wind Swept Fields stadium has 22,500 seats. They have sold 16,755 tickets. How many seats are still available?

   22,500 − 16,755 = 5745;
   5745 seats

2. Mr. Avalon's has planted one million, two hundred thousand vegetable seeds. How many more seeds does he need to plant to reach 3 million?

   3,000,000 − 1,200,000 =
   1,800,000; 1,800,000 seeds

3. Lauren bought three shirts that each cost $22.75. She paid with 4 twenty-dollar bills. How much change did Lauren get back?

   4 × $20.00 = $80.00; 3 × $22.75 =
   $68.25; $80.00 − $68.25 =
   $11.75; $11.75

4. Danny spent $98.40 on 4 bales of hay. How much money did Danny spend on each bale of hay?

   $98.40 ÷ 4 = $24.60

5. What is the sum of 150, 250, 350, 450, 550, 650, 750, 850, and 950?

   150 + 250 + 350 + 450 + 550 +
   650 + 750 + 850 + 950 = 4950

6. How many cars will the soccer team need to take to the game if there are 18 players on the team, and each car fits 5 players?

   $18 ÷ 5 = 3 R3; 4 cars

7. Randy sold half of his jacks. After buying 24 more, he has 38 jacks. How many jacks did he have in the beginning?

   38 − 24 = 14; 14 × 2 = 28;
   28 jacks

8. Suchin bought an mp3 player that holds 3,000 songs. After putting an equal number of songs from her 2 brothers on it, she has room for 800 more songs. How many songs did she get from each brother?

   3000 − 800 = 2200;
   2200 ÷ 2 = 1100; 1100 songs

9. The Wall family bought 8 trees. The first one cost $36.00, and the second one cost $34.00. If this pattern continued, how much did the Wall family spend in all?

   36 + 34 + 32 + 30 + 28 + 26 +
   24 + 22 = 232; $232